Gnomes of the Night
The Spadefoot Toads

Gnomes of the Night

The Spadefoot Toads

by Arthur N. Bragg

Foreword by Dr. Hobart M. Smith

Philadelphia
University of Pennsylvania Press

7472

Printed in the United States of America

Dedicated to my friend and former coworker with
the spadefoots, Dr. Charles Clinton Smith Sr.

Contents

Illustrations

The illustrations appear as a group following page 96.

Couch's Spadefoot (*Scaphiopus couchi* Baird) just after being removed from its burrow.

The same individual after some minutes in bright light.

An adult and a halfgrown juvenile of the Plains Spadefoot.

Couch's Spadefoot from southwestern Oklahoma showing the characteristic mottling on the back.

A characteristic breeding site of Hurter's Spadefoot.

Portion of a clutch of eggs.

Tadpoles of Hurter's Spadefoot.

A tadpole of Hurter's Spadefoot feeding on particles in an aquarium.

Pool in which stalked eggs of *Scaphiopus bombifrons* were found.

A typical breeding site of the Plains Spadefoot.

Pool containing tadpoles of *Scaphiopus hammondi*.

A typical breeding site of Hammond's Spadefoot.

The hind feet of two spadefoots, showing the difference in the spade in the two species groups.

Looking directly into the open mouths of two tadpoles of *Scaphiopus bombifrons* to show variations.

Masses of Hurter's Spadefoot tadpoles.

Masses of dead tadpoles of the Plains Spadefoot.

Pool in oak-shinnery in western Oklahoma which contained tadpoles of the Plains Spadefoot.

Breeding site of Couch's Spadefoot in southwestern Oklahoma.

Aggregated tadpoles of the Plains Spadefoot at shore line.

Map 1. Approximate geographic distribution of spadefoots of subgenus Scaphiopus.

Map 2. Approximate geographic distribution of spadefoots of subgenus Spea in U.S.A.

Foreword

FIRST AND FOREMOST, TO THIS READER "GNOMES OF THE NIGHT" is a revealing account of the scientific method in actual operation, not solely in theory—*in vivo,* as it were, instead of *in vitro* as generally presented. It shows how a scientific theory often grows; how a scientist's thinking processes operate in his area of scientific endeavor; what pitfalls beset the path to induction of sound conclusions contingent upon numerous variables; and it shows how an open mind must be maintained even in reference to seemingly impregnable concepts. Few works make so plain to any who might read them what the scientific method really means.

Secondly, this book is notable as the most complete account in existence of a strange group of animals with unusually numerous interesting facets in its life history. This account may, indeed, justly be viewed as the foremost message of the *Gnomes of the Night,* for it is completely fascinating in itself. To me, however, this seems, despite its clear appeal, but the attractive wrapping for a more subtly compelling achievement in presentation of the scientific method.

Thirdly, the *Gnomes of the Night* is virtually unique among accounts on specific groups of reptiles or amphibians for its absorbing readability. Formal descriptions or data or both so dominate most accounts of these animals that it is indeed a rare treat for specialist and catholic reader alike to be able comfortably to read the entire work straight through—to absorb truly novel information in a welcomingly palatable form. But the author has long held the enviable reputation among his fellow specialists of producing the most regularly readable yet rewarding of papers.

In each of the three cited respects this book is in a class virtually by itself, and to combine all three under one cover makes it unquestionably exceptional. It richly merits the time required to read it, and the space in the mind and on the bookshelves of any literate person, zoologist or not.

Hobart M. Smith.
University of Illinois

Preface

SEVERAL GROUPS OF ANIMALS WHOSE HABITS ARE PECULIARLY
different from what one might expect, *a priori,* have stimulated
those who have studied them to write about their peculiarities
to provide an opportunity for people to become better
acquainted with some of their more striking neighbors. Some
books are excellent in their making the animals concerned
understandable and interesting. Others are merely exasperat-
ing because they are filled with anthropomorphisms and superficially stated half truths.

Such a peculiar group of animals constitutes the subject of
the present account. The spadefoot toad's story is (or so it
seems to me) sufficiently interesting in itself, and I have not
attempted to embellish it with flowery popularizations refer-
ring directly or indirectly to man's actions or desires. I have
avoided using more technical terms than appeared necessary,
but I have introduced these freely where they seemed to make
the story clearer and more nearly true.

I have attempted a straightforward, factual account of this
small group of species, drawing upon the technical literature as
well as upon my own wide experience with certain species of
the spadefoots. Also, since mere facts have little meaning, I
have introduced my interpretations of the peculiarities of
spadefoot habits for what they may be worth. I do this fully
aware that some modifications of my interpretation may be
forthcoming—indeed I invite them—that, through discussion
and further experience with these animals, may eventually
emerge a closer approximation to the truth about them than

13

any of us now may have. No one, I think, least of all me, believes that the last word has been said about my "gnomes of the night."

The book is primarily addressed to all who are interested in animal habits in relation to their adaptive significance in evolution. Details of structure are given only second place at best. Taxonomy is mentioned (and used) throughout but only as a convenience upon which to discuss differences in habits, habitats and ecological "preferences" exhibited by the animals.

A secondary objective of the book is to illustrate how a naturalist works; my earlier frustrations, blunders and misconceptions in the study of the spadefoots serving as examples of how depth and breadth of understanding are gradually derived by persistent observations. I am not embarrassed by these mistakes, for I understand well the human proclivity for error. No scientist can ever be sure that he is wholly right about anything until all possibilities are understood—and by no means are all things known, even now, about the gnomes of the night. Full truth is hard to come by in any subject.

The common names used for spadefoots of the United States are those recommended recently by a committee of the American Society of Ichthyologists and Herpetologists, which, for the sake of uniformity, I wholly endorse.

Many popular books in natural history do not include a bibliography and often do not state the sources of many statements made. I think this is a mistake. I give a list of references including all or most of the more important studies made so far on the spadefoots. It is not intended to be completely exhaustive, however, omitting such things as several minor reports on range extensions and other minor notes.

Acknowledgments

ACKNOWLEDGMENTS ARE DUE AND GLADLY GIVEN FOR THE help of the following: Dr. Herman Forest and Dr. James C. Colbert, respectively of the Departments of Plant Sciences and Chemistry, University of Oklahoma, and my wife (Mary G. Bragg), and Mr. Charles West for critical reading of the manuscript; Mr. Marlin Dobry, Dr. Charles C. Smith, the late professor Otis M. King, and Dr. Aaron Wasserman for illustrations; also the last three mentioned for clarification of ideas in personal discussions; and my son, William N. Bragg, for much help in field work through several years. My researches on the spadefoots have been supported by the University of Oklahoma Biological Survey and I have received much help and encouragement from its director, Dr. Carl D. Riggs, as well as from its former director, Dr. A. Richards.

Norman, Oklahoma
October, 1962.

Introduction

THIS LITTLE VOLUME STEMS FROM MY DESIRE TO SHARE THE results of a personal quest. Because of this, I hope to be pardoned if I outline the background leading up to it—factors in my personal life which led me into the study of natural history in general and, finally, to my study of the spadefoot toads, a small group of American animals which, because of their secretive and burrowing habits, I here call the gnomes of the night.

Strangely enough the story begins in one of the very few regions of the United States in which none of these animals occur—south central Maine. In the spring of 1909, I was living on a small Maine farm located just above the common valley of two adjacent and nearly parallel streams whose courses joined below the farm yard and flowed as one into Great Moose Lake a mile or so beyond. The location is in the township of Harmony, Somerset County, and quite near a small village known as Mainstream. At this time, about a half-century ago, this region was almost primitive in its wildness, and I, an eleven-year-old boy, was as wild and as free as any of the numerous creatures of the adjoining woods and fields.

The winter had been severe with deep snows. In the spring, the two streams, failing to carry the burden of the sudden melt, overflowed their banks to merge as a single extensive sheet of water just below the farm buildings. Various wild ducks and Canada geese on their spring migration northward

17

found this an excellent resting and feeding ground, and later, when the water receded, I caught sizeable fish with my bare hands, trapped in any of several pools left in the lower places by the rapidly receding water.

Sometime in April I began to hear strange sounds coming from the largest of these pools during warmer evenings—a guttural chuckling which I had never noticed before. My attempt to trace the source of these sounds started a chain of events which has largely determined the whole pattern of my professional career and finally led me to the gnomes of the night.

What I had heard was the mating call of the common leopard frogs (*Rana pipiens* Schreber). I saw their breeding reactions and later found their eggs. As I watched the development, hatching of these eggs into tadpoles and the growth and metamorphosis of these tadpoles into young frogs in mid-summer, I developed so great an interest in the habits of frogs and related animals that it has never left me throughout a long lifetime.

In the subsequent years of my boyhood and adolescence, I spent long hours with the frogs and toads. With no formal training and without books or adults who paid this interest of mine any attention, I learned from obvious differences in habits and habitat to distinguish the two species of spotted frogs occurring in Maine. I also distinguished the bronze frog (*Rana clamitans melanota*) from the bullfrog (*Rana catesbeiana*), two species which were confounded by most of the adults of my limited world.

As I progressed through secondary school, college, graduate studies and finally into university teaching in zoology, I learned nothing which should lead me to believe that l did not understand the fundamental principles of frog and toad breeding. Indeed, I made successful use of these principles in New

England, Maryland, and Wisconsin through many seasons in securing specimens for study or teaching. When, therefore, I first came to the University of Oklahoma in 1934 and the next spring wished to find toad's and frog's eggs for study, I expected to secure them easily, merely as a matter of routine. But a month's search revealed not a single egg! I was chagrined and puzzled. Surely there must be amphibians in Oklahoma—why couldn't I find them?

In late April I got my answer from the frogs and toads themselves. The spring rains started, and immediately more frogs and, especially, toads appeared than I had believed possible to be supported anywhere per unit of land. Temporary pools swarmed with toads and toad-like forms. Each night, and sometimes throughout the day, a deafening roar, punctuated with squeaking and buzzing breeding calls, composed of the voices of animals of at least six species, each present by the hundreds or thousands, emphasized that I still had something to learn. But I still thought only in terms of a different locality having unfamiliar species, not in terms of different principles involved.

As my observations were intensified, my interest grew apace, for soon I discovered that I was learning things not only new to *me* but also new to science. Accordingly, since this first introduction to the amphibian choruses of the grasslands, I have done little else professionally than study the habits, distribution and evolution of the amphibians of Oklahoma, and now, after almost twenty-five years of this, I am still finding things about them which were unknown.

Among the many kinds heard that first April night was the loud, harsh and guttural "waa, wah" of the Plains Spadefoot as hundreds of their little grayish bodies bobbed about on the wind-swept surface of a flooded field. This served as my introduction to the gnomes of the night. Later I was to learn that three other species of spadefoots also occur in Oklahoma, one of them having just been reported for the first time and within about ten miles of where I then lived. Further to emphasize the great gulf between what I had *thought* I knew and what I *really* knew, I have only to state that it took me four more years to find a specimen of this second local species and ten more years before I could catch them breeding or find their tadpoles—yet I now know them to be very abundant here. I just did not know where, when, or how to look.

During the better part of the last 20 years or so, I have studied diligently all species of the Amphibia in Oklahoma (about 50 kinds), and of them all none are so surprising as the spadefoots. Scarcely a year passes that some new phenomenon in one species or another of them does not show up. And, still, just as I think that now (at last!) I have finally solved the mystery of their life story, I find some that quite obviously have not read my scientific papers! They just do not behave as I had supposed, and I have to start all over again. But actually I have, of course, learned a great deal in my more than two decades-long quest of the gnomes of the night. It is what I have learned, supplemented by what others have reported about them, that I wish to share with my readers. This will be seasoned by what I think *now* that the observations mean.

I do not intend this to be a technically exhaustive account of the spadefoots: but I do intend it to be accurate. Accordingly, I think it wise to begin with a few paragraphs of more or less technical details concerning their naming and distribution.

Gnomes of the Night
The Spadefoot Toads

I

History, Classification and Distribution of Spadefoots

IN 1835, RICHARD HARLAN, A PIONEER AMERICAN NATURALIST, discovered and described from South Carolina what he thought to be an unknown frog. This, we now know, was the first American spadefoot ever seen, at present called the Eastern Spadefoot *(Scaphiopus holbrooki holbrooki)*. Nineteen years passed before the second species was found, this time in collections from Mexico and Texas. It was described and named by Spencer F. Baird of the then new National Museum of the Smithsonian Institution in Washington, D. C. We now know this species as Couch's Spadefoot *(S. couchi)*. Another species showed up in California five years later (i.e., in 1859). This now is called Hammond's Spadefoot *(S. hammondi hammondi)* also described by Baird. A fourth type, so much like Hammond's Spadefoot as to cause much later confusion, was found on the Missouri and Platt rivers in 1863. This we now know as the Plains Spadefoot *(S. bombifrons)*. It was described by Edward D. Cope, naturalist and editor, then one of the few leaders in American natural history. The next spadefoot to be described was from the beginning a

23

questionable form. It was found on Key West, Florida, and described by H. Garman in 1877 as *S. albus*. Most now believe it to be only a local variant of the Eastern Spadefoot (see Duellman, 1955), but when one desires to speak of it separately from this, it is called the Key West Spadefoot. In 1883, still another one was found in Utah, described by Cope as *Scaphiopus intermontanus,* now known commonly as the Great Basin Spadefoot; and in 1863 Cope had named still another *(S. multiplicatus)* from Mexico. This, which we may call the Mexican spadefoot, is the only one not found in the United States. The list of known living spadefoots as of now was completed in 1910 when John K. Strecker, Jr. of Waco, Texas named *S. hurterii,* now usually considered as a subspecies of the eastern species and called Hurter's spadefoot, *(S. holbrooki hurteri).* Recently a new subspecies of *S. couchi* has been described. I omit this because I have not yet seen specimens of it.

To summarize, this gives us eight named living forms, all from North America, and all described between 1835 and 1910. Since the Key West Spadefoot is probably only a variant of the eastern one *(S. h. holbrooki),* seven kinds are now recognized. In addition, several fossil species are known which we will not discuss here.

The spadefoots may be separated into two groups of species, each characterized by certain peculiarities not shown by the other. One of these groups is composed of animals of medium size, of generally lighter coloration, and with a short, wide, digging tubercle on each ankle (the spade). These also have tadpoles which grow to large size. The second group is contrasted by larger adult size, darker coloration, a longer or narrower, sickle-shaped spade and small tadpoles. Cope long ago suggested that these differences were of sufficient magnitude to warrant separation of the two groups into separate genera (*Spea* for the first and *Scaphiopus—sensu stricto—*for the second). He was not generally followed in this; but in recent years the name *Spea* is reviving. Tanner (1939) called it a subgenus within *Scaphiopus (sensu lato),* and I agreed (Bragg, 1944–45) as did Stebbins (1951) and a few others. More recently Brown (1950), followed by Smith (1956) has returned to Cope's idea. Schmidt (1953) did not, however, use this scheme in the 6th edition of the check list of names followed by most students of the group in the United States, nor did he recognize subgenera.

These details are presented merely to show that even in the technical naming of spadefoots there is real difference of opinions of authorities about them, and, more important, to point out the fact that we all still have much to learn about their lives, evolution and nature. Even the larger group (the family) to which they should be assigned is uncertain, some insisting that they constitute a family all by themselves (the *Scaphiopodidae*), others that they should be placed with Old World forms somewhat similar, as is done below. Tentatively, and with full recognition of the uncertainties involved, we may for our purpose here accept the following grouping:

Class Amphibia
　Order Salientia
　　Family Pelobatidae
　　　Genus Scaphiopus
　　　　Subgenus Scaphiopus
　　　　　1.　*Scaphiopus holbrooki holbrooki (Harlan)*
　　　　　　(Eastern Spadefoot)
　　　　　2.　*Scaphiopus holbrooki hurteri* Strecker
　　　　　　(Hurter's Spadefoot)
　　　　　3.　*Scaphiopus couchi* Baird
　　　　　　(Couch's Spadefoot)
　　　　Subgenus Spea

1. *Scaphiopus bombifrons* Cope
   (Plains Spadefoot)
2. *Scaphiopus multiplicatus* Cope
   (Mexican Spadefoot)
3. *Scaphiopus hammondi hammondi* Baird
   (Hammond's Spadefoot)
4. *Scaphiopus hammondi intermontanus*
   Cope (Great Basin Spadefoot)

In most parts of the United States, at least one kind of spadefoot occurs. In a recent paper I expressed this as follows : "Collectively, the spadefoots cover most regions of central and southern North America, north to near Boston, Massachusetts, in the East and to southern British Columbia in the west, south to the region of Mexico City [actually somewhat beyond this]. In the United States only the northern states east of the Great Plains apparently lack some species of spadefoot. None are known in northern New England, much of New York, Michigan, and Wisconsin." Only one of them, the Mexican Spadefoot, does not occur in this country. On the other hand, along the Mexican border, especially in the Southwest, three of them occur in both countries, thus giving Mexico four kinds (see maps 1 and 2).

But merely to give their geographic distributions based upon the artificial, politically determined boundaries is insufficient to understand the spadefoots' distribution. We must also consider the region of their probable origin and the adaptations which they, like other animals, have made since the first spadefoot was formed.

Dr. Tanner in the paper quoted earlier concluded that the first home of the spadefoots was in the Southwest and the details of their distribution and habits at present strongly suggest that this is correct. The whole region east of eastern Arkansas contains only one kind, the Eastern Spadefoot, if we disregard the Key West form. On the other hand, at the eastern edge of the Southwest, Oklahoma has four. New Mexico has certainly three and possibly another, Texas has four and a possible fifth. California has three, but from approximately the latitude of San Francisco northward, only one occurs, this one just barely entering Canada to the north of Washington. Another enters Canada from Montana. Several of their distributions overlap. For example, Hurter's spadefoot occurs abundantly throughout the eastern halves of Oklahoma and Texas. Couch's Spadefoot occurs with it in some regions of south central Texas and in at least one place in northern Texas (at Nacona) near Oklahoma. These two are not known to occur in the same regions in Oklahoma but they may later be found to do so near the Red River in the south-western part of the state. The Plains spadefoot occurs in several places with one or more of Hurter's, Couch's and Hammond's Spadefoots, but apparently nowhere do all four of these occupy the same territory.

The reason for the overlapping may be found in the adaptations to different environments, even in the same regions. For example, Wasserman (1957) recently pointed out that Hurter's Spadefoot in Texas lives mostly in areas of sandy soil, whereas Couch's Spadefoot is not usually found in regions having much sand. In northeastern Oklahoma and western Arkansas the former occurs on other types of soil, but elsewhere in Oklahoma it seems to prefer sandy areas as in Texas. The Plains Spadefoot and Hammond's Spadefoot seldom are to be found in regions of sandy soils, and when they are the population is usually small. Both of these live in areas of "tight" soils, for the most part, and their ranges overlap by several hundred miles in western Oklahoma, Texas, at least the eastern part of New Mexico, and parts of Arizona.

Because of these soil preferences, disturbances by man's

activities have sometimes allowed mixing of species which probably would not have occurred under natural conditions. In Dr. Wasserman's study, for example, he found hybrids between Couch's and Hurter's spadefoots at Austin, Texas, in a small disturbed area. Apparently the disturbance of the soil of a park had made conditions right so that both species now occupy the area and occasionally interbreed.

In central Oklahoma, Hurter's Spadefoot occurs in partially wooded areas of sandy soil but stops abruptly at the junction of the tighter clay soil supporting grassland. However, the wide, sandy flood plains of the prairie rivers maintain small populations of this animal far west of the usual habitat. But the Plains Spadefoot, very abundant above the rivers on the prairie, rarely if ever occupies the flood plains in central Oklahoma, although it does so on the Arkansas River at Tulsa, very near the eastern limit of its range. But in northwestern Oklahoma, where extensive sandy prairies occur (as well as in some areas of small oaks known as shinnery, Fig. 18), tadpoles of the Plains Spadefoot are often abundant in temporary pools and Hurter's Spadefoot is unknown. It therefore seems that type of soil tends to control the distribution of spadefoots in some areas but that elsewhere other factors are involved. The animals do not like too wet an environment and often die if crowded and wet, perhaps from the effect of their own waste products. This is about all that is known specifically concerning the ecological control of spadefoot distribution at the present time, but it is sufficient at least to indicate that geographic and ecological distributions are not the same things. Clearly, related animals of many kinds may live in the same region yet may not compete with each other for food or living room because they occupy different ecological niches. The spadefoots conform to this general rule.

II

Some Peculiarities of Spadefoots

THE ADULT SPADEFOOT IS ABOUT 3 TO 4 INCHES LONG, SHORT,
squat, and toad-like in form. In all their species, the adult male
averages smaller than the adult female in which they are like
most other North American frogs and toads. Their colors vary
greatly. Spadefoots of the Spea group are typically gray or
brown (sometimes mottled in these colors) and some kinds may
have small red spots irregularly scattered on the back (especially when juvenile) and sometimes white or light cream-
colored markings. Some individuals are very light colored,
others much darker, and, like many other Amphibia, the
individual animal can change its color in response to environmental stimuli. The overall general effect, disregarding variations, is of a small, rather light colored, toad-like animal with
a gray or brown back and white, unmarked belly. In contrast,
members of the other group (Couch's, Hurter's and the
Eastern Spadefoots) are larger and, while varying much, tend
mostly toward a dark green or blackish green on the back with
characteristic mottling or markings in lighter or darker colors.
Couch's Spadefoot sometimes has a few irregularly placed
dark spots but often is mottled in lighter color on dark back-

29

ground, whereas the others usually have hourglass shaped light areas on the back. Again, disregarding variations, the overall general effect is a larger toad-like animal of dark green with characteristic dorsal markings and a white belly. The lighter, hourglass-shaped region seems widest and most prominent in the Key West Spadefoot from which its scientific name (*albus,* white) is derived.

In most spadefoots the skin is soft, thin and without the many wart-like glands of the familiar garden toads. The Mexican form, however, is rather warty and rough, and some of the others have small glands (warts) or special paired glandular areas on the breast region—structures which others lack. The latter are often more prominent on large individuals where their positions suggest the flattened nipples of a mammal. The whole skin of the spadefoot tends to be moist and slimy, more like that of the common frog than of a garden toad.

The secretion of the skin glands (whether these glands are seen externally or not) consists of mucus mixed with other substances whose chemical natures, so far as I know, have never been determined. (See, however, Blair, Hargraves, and Chen, 1940.) It differs slightly in the two groups, but in both is irritating to the membranes of the human nose and mouth. The secretion has a musty, rather unpleasant odor and one of the nastiest tastes of which I am aware (I know because I tried it once and my scientific curiosity was well satisfied). Presumably this secretion is protective against predators. In several species it has been noticed in handling spadefoots that this secretion is more copious in females than in males. No one knows why this is so; but several years ago I offered some speculations about it which are here repeated for what they may be worth.

It is well known that evolutionary forces of nature have produced behavior patterns and their emotional counterparts in animals leading toward individual survival. Self-preservation has often been called the "first law of life." But it is also just as obvious that these drives are really aimed more at the survival of the *species* than to that of any individual. To use a common figure, nature is not primarily interested in *individual* survival but in *racial* survival. Survival of the individual sufficiently long to reproduce is the real aim as evidenced by many organisms (mayflies, cicadas, many moths, and the annual plants including the common garden pea, for example), all of which grow fast to reproductive age, reproduce and then die naturally and quickly. In other words, self preservation is *not* the first law of life in any species, including man. If there be any one first law it is the preservation of the race (i.e., species) to which an organism belongs and all of its nature does its best to further this end, even though often and perhaps always (excepting man), blindly and unconsciously.

If now we assume that the more copious dermal secretions of the female spadefoot give it more and better protection than the male possesses, we seem to be saying that the individual female is more important to racial survival than is the male. To continue the figure, nature considers her of greater value than the male for the survival of the species and has, therefore, given her greater protection. Since both male and female spadefoots are necessary to reproduce other spadefoots, each contributing equally to the heredity of the young, how can this be justified?

The answer is really simple, though not easy to state simply. Many factors are involved but they all pertain to the difference between the male's and female's contribution to the reproductive process, namely the sperm cell of the male and the egg of the female. A basic female function, from the cellular level to the most complex society, is the care and feeding of the young. In spadefoots (and many other animals) this begins with the production of the egg. This cell has, packed within it, more concentrated food for the "anticipated" embryo than it has of living substance. To secure this nutriment and to concentrate it, the female spadefoot must eat enormously of its normal insect food which it can get only by being at the surface of the ground and exposed to predators. A better idea of the importance of this will be realized if we know that a single female may produce as many as 3600 of such eggs at one laying. One Hurter's Spadefoot produced approximately this number (Bragg, 1950d) in what was thought to be a clutch of usual size. On the other hand, the male sex cells are tiny and with almost no stored materials. The male needs food mostly for his own growth and maintenance and does not need to feed as often (or as well). Hence he needs less protection with his less exposure.

This argument rests on the assumption that female spadefoots are more active in feeding than are males. It has never been proven that this is actually the case and the only observations of consequence appertaining (Pearson, 1955), while they do not deny this possibility, they do not particularly support this assumption either for the Eastern Spadefoot in Florida. Nevertheless, the possibility should not be ruled out completely for all spadefoots, since habits of even closely related species may differ in different habitats, and I myself have observed that female garden toads (*Bufo*) feed more than males in Oklahoma. Also, what pertains to one species of spadefoot may not pertain to another. We need further observations here.

Returning now to other peculiarities of the spadefoots, it is to be noted that the hind feet are markedly webbed like those of a frog, although the toes and legs are much shorter, more like those of the garden toads (*Bufo*). As earlier mentioned, in the ankle region of each leg, a dark prominence with a sharp cutting edge occurs by use of which the animal is able to dig itself rapidly into the ground. This spade is narrow, rather long and slightly curved in one group (Subgenus Scaphiopus); short, more rounded, and wider in the other (Spea) as shown in Fig. 14. In the adult males, the fingers have horny growths which enable them to retain a better grip on the slippery body of a female during fertilization.

The thin, slimy skin and markedly webbed feet suggest that, like common frogs (*Rana*), one would expect to find spadefoots in moist places such as in swamps, on river and lake margins and about streams, where moisture is easily available and desiccation could be avoided. This impression is enhanced by the fact that, also like frogs, a spadefoot dies rather quickly in a warm, dry atmosphere, obviously from loss of water through the skin.

Yet, this is just the type of habitat that is *not* occupied by any of the spadefoot toads and a captive often dies if kept in very wet soil for any considerable time. In fact, as a group, they tend to inhabit some of the driest regions of North America and they seldom if ever enter water except to breed. The real home of the spadefoots is in deserts, semideserts, or grassland areas such as found from Oklahoma and western Kansas southwestward in the prairies and plains. One can almost say that the drier the region, the more likely will one or more species of spadefoots be found in it, often represented by many individuals. It is partly for this reason that Dr. Tanner concluded that the spadefoots probably originated in the Sonoran region near the Mexican border and spread out and evolved from there to occupy other areas. The Eastern Spadefoot (including the Key West form) is, in some respects, a desert animal out of place as will become more evident later when we discuss spadefoot breeding habits and tadpole behavior.

How can these animals, which are so easily killed by desiccation, thrive in such dry places? They do it by two means : (1) They are almost completely nocturnal in their habits, seldom out in daylight (and if so, usually only after rains or floods); (2) They are very efficient burrowers, using their sharp spades to sink deeply into the soil where it is moist and cool. Furthermore, a spadefoot may remain in its burrow below the surface for weeks or even months at a time if necessary and then emerge quickly for feeding as conditions become more favorable at the surface. Captive spadefoots which I have studied have been found just below the surface of the earth when it was moist but as far down as they could get (two or three feet in some cases) as the soil became drier and I know of one case wherein a spadefoot was discovered 15 feet below the surface under natural conditions. Occasionally peculiar things happen. For example, just over 30 years ago some hard clay balls were dug out by an excavation crew in southwestern Oklahoma, each of which had a spadefoot inside it (Decker, 1930). There was great speculation as to how long they had lived in this condition and some even thought in geological terms, visualizing these animals as having lived thousands of years in these enclosures. The spadefoots *were* trapped, but the explanation is probably much simpler. Clay had filtered into the burrows and its particles had become entangled and held by the mucous secretions and packed by the movement of the animals. This clay then had hardened as the soil became dry, thus entrapping the spadefoots. It is not certain whether these animals would have been able to free themselves if the soil had again become thoroughly wet, but I can understand how they might have done so.

Some years ago I was visited by newspaper reporters and asked to identify a toad-like animal which had been dug up while removing the concrete runway of an air field near Oklahoma City. The previous day the newspaper had run a story of this toad which, it was thought, must have been in the ground ever since the concrete was laid several years before. It was, of course, a spadefoot, and it had *not* been under the concrete all of this time. One of two things had occurred— either (1) the animal had found a crack in the concrete and had entered it to make its burrow or (2) it had dug in at the side and burrowed its way to where it was found. The former is the more probable but the latter is possible, since it is known that captive spadefoots, even when free to come to the surface, sometimes burrow about considerably under ground. I have found them doing so on several occasions, although this is not their usual behavior.

BURROWS :

I had often wondered if a spadefoot utilizes the same burrow night after night during times of feeding but was unsuccessful in my attempts to learn much about it in nature. Captive spadefoots were placed in a large enclosure, essentially a large concrete box, filled with earth. These were watched for some time each night during one summer. I soon found that specimens of one kind at least (Hurter's Spadefoot) used the same burrow for many days and I inferred that they probably did so under natural conditions.

Some time later, in a very detailed and valuable study of the Eastern Spadefoot in Florida, Pearson (1955) showed that considerable homing occurs. Each individual in the study areas used seemed to have a home burrow from which it emerged to feed and to which it returned day after day. Occasionally a toad moved and dug another burrow and some individuals seemed to have more than one burrow, using one for a time and then the other. Furthermore, each animal seemed to have a home range out of which it seldom went except for breeding purposes : and the individual ranges were so spaced that no spadefoot interfered much with others. This behavior results, automatically, in the available feeding area near each burrow becoming the "property" of the owner of the burrow and in the whole feeding area being effectively utilized by the population as a whole. Whether or not other types of spadefoots have this sort of behavior appears, at present, to be unknown.

FOOD AND FEEDING :

The spadefoot's food is largely made up of ground-dwelling insects, spiders, and other small arthropods. They eat moths when they can catch them and there is much evidence that, except for size of food objects, there is little selection among the arthropods they ingest. There may be some selection, however. I once had a dozen or so very young Plains Spadefoots in a container and was testing the things that they would eat. I offered them spiders and many kinds of small beetles, bugs, ants, moths, and other insects, all of which they ate readily. Then, one day, I put into the box several specimens of a small black ant of a kind not previously offered them. Immediately several of the baby toads (then about as large as the last section of one's little finger) attacked them. As each took an ant into its mouth it suddenly exploded into activity, clawing at its mouth to free itself from the ant and not ceasing until it finally succeeded. Thereafter, I could never induce these particular individuals to attack this kind of ant, though they continued to eat other kinds of ants I offered them.

This observation is not only interesting in showing that some ants apparently have an effective defense against the predatory activities of young Plains Spadefoots, but also in demonstrating that these toads can learn by trial and error, at least to some extent, and that they can do so with only one unpleasant experience.

Later I made observations which seemed to offer some reason for this quick learning. Captive Plains Spadefoots, of about the same size and age when first confined as those mentioned above, were watched each night throughout the better part of a summer. During this time they grew appreciably, of course, and I was able to note any differences in feeding which might develop with increasing size and age. From watching the adults, I already knew the general method of their feeding.

I found that their selection of food objects on the basis of size was very marked. The small individuals attacked only small objects and, as they grew, attempted ingestion of larger and larger insects until, finally, they were attempting to capture arthropods the size of June beetles and larger moths. I also noted that a preference was soon developed for the largest food objects capable of being swallowed at any one spadefoot size. Tiny insects which had been ingested greedily by the small spadefoots went untouched by larger ones of this same species, provided that the latter had a good supply of larger arthropods available to them. These animals, therefore, had learned to select larger food objects. Since each large insect represents more food than a small one, this learning is a part of the adaptive response of the spadefoot for biological efficiency. Not only does it serve the spadefoot physiologically in its conservation of energy (it takes almost as much effort for a toad to capture a small as a large insect) but also it is protective as well. The animal can fill its stomach sooner by ingesting its meal quickly and in larger pieces and then retreating to its burrow where it is safer than at the surface. The spadefoots do exactly this when the stomach is filled.

Another and in some respects more interesting phenomenon emerged from these observations on the feeding of growing

Plains Spadefoots. This involved selection of another kind and emphasizes the sensory cues used in this selection. In order to make this clear, I must first describe the action of a spadefoot in feeding.

In nature, a hunting spadefoot hops slowly along, pausing here and there, with eyes ever alert for movement. In captivity, it soon learns to remain quiet for longer periods, awaiting the insects attracted to a light above its place of confinement. In either case, any movement that it sees usually causes it to become motionless. If the moving object is large, such as a cow, dog, man or auto, the animal senses danger and usually remains still until approached very closely, although this varies with the species of spadefoot. Hurter's spadefoot, for example, will often enter its burrow if it is nearby or start digging into the ground for concealment if in captivity. In nature one can often step on the animals without their moving until touched. On the other hand, if the object is small, as another small amphibian or an insect on the ground, the spadefoot becomes very alert, orients its head toward the movement, sometimes crawls forward a little and waits with its gaze resting intently on the object. If it is a suitable food object (a small beetle or spider, for example, of the right size for it to ingest) the toad may do one of two things—attack immediately or await a second movement by the potential prey. It usually waits if the movement has stopped and is again started. The toads are obviously very much attracted by small moving objects but they usually need a continuous movement like that of a crawling beetle or a second movement if the one which just attracted them has stopped.

Now the interesting thing is that if the movement is caused by a smaller toad (even one much smaller than beetles which the individual has been ingesting) after a close look the animal usually backs or turns away and pays it no further attention.

It behaves as though it recognizes another toad as not being suitable food, and this is true not only of its own kind but of young garden toads (*Bufo*) as well. It is not likely that the spadefoot can sense at a distance the protective dermal secretions, although this is possible. If not, then it probably reacts to different types of movement of its potential prey. In any case, the spadefoots which I have watched did not attack others of their kind, regardless of size, and in this they are quite different from most frogs (*Rana*) which eat smaller frogs or toads, whether of their own species or another. Expressed in rather anthropomorphic language, one may say adult and juvenile spadefoots are more discerning and selective in their feeding than are frogs. Incidentally, I have found also that some of the garden toads *(Bufo)* are like the spadefoots and unlike the frogs in this characteristic (although it does not follow that all are). I know Hurter's and Couch's spadefoots to behave in this manner, also, and one would expect other species to be the same. However, I know of no observations on other species and it cannot be too strongly emphasized that it is never sound to assume that one species will necessarily behave as another without checking to be sure.

SEASONAL ACTIVITIES :

Spadefoots are necessarily somewhat seasonal in their activities because of their constant danger of desiccation when at the surface of the ground. This danger, of course, depends on intensity of local rainfall, evaporation rate, temperature, and wind, all of which vary markedly over a large continent— locally, seasonally and otherwise. It is, therefore, impossible to generalize as to the seasonal activity of the spadefoots as a group. Nevertheless, there are some things that can be said about it.

At least the Eastern Spadefoot and the Plains Spadefoot and perhaps others emerge in spring only when the ground moisture has reached a proper level (Ball, 1936; Trowbridge and Trowbridge, 1937). Spadefoot activity is inhibited also by cold so that no date of spring emergence can be given as typical even for a local region. In a cold, wet spring the animals may be as late as in a warm dry one : but they may be exceptionally early in a warm, moist season. Latitude, of course, influences these conditions so that one expects on the average that a wintering Eastern Spadefoot in Virginia or Florida will emerge in the spring before one in Connecticut or Massachusetts; and in moist regions of the South they might be active all winter. In the Southwest, where torrential rains are commonly associated with spring and temperature fluctuates widely and quickly, some spadefoots may be first out as early as January in some years or as late as mid-April in others in a given locality.

I know of no observations on the method of spring emergence in nature. Captive spadefoots of three species (Plains, Hurter's and Couch's) which I have kept over the winter in a large concrete container for several years in central Oklahoma have emerged gradually during most years. Typically, on warm nights in March or early April, some of the animals have approached the surface and often broken through the hard-packed soil without actually coming out. (Sometimes they lie for long periods with only the snout or snout and eyes showing.) Presumably this gives them better access to the oxygen of the air as their metabolic processes increase with the warming of the soil. They may emerge shortly thereafter (one or a few nights later) or remain in the burrows for several weeks more, apparently depending upon conditions of temperature and moisture and, perhaps, barometric pressure. Once they have broken through the surface, however, they tend to keep the soil above them loose by their activities below ground.

Whether or not spadefoots have already emerged from the winter burrow, a heavy rain at air temperatures above about 10° C. (=about 52° F.) from late February onward usually stimulates emergence, at least of Hurter's and the Plains forms in Oklahoma, but a light rain will do so only if soil moisture is already adequate. Further study is needed to elucidate the exact conditions. The one thing certain is that spadefoots react markedly and quickly both to moisture conditions and to temperatures.

Since in the habitat of a typical spadefoot, the optimum relations between these two influences typically occurs at night, the long evolution of the spadefoots has made them essentially nocturnal animals. An adult spadefoot toad is almost never voluntarily active in daylight except, rarely, during breeding as discussed on page 34 and occasionally on very humid days. Some types, at least, may retreat from light (negative photo-taxis) although this has never, as far as I know, been studied carefully. Captive adult males of Hurter's Spadefoot kept in the container mentioned earlier have always been at the surface in greater numbers than usual when there has been no artificial light above it at night. Furthermore, this has not been true of other species with them (but in another compartment of the container) nor of specimens of the common garden toads (*Bufo*) also present at the same time.

Having once emerged from winter burrows in the spring-time, each spadefoot tends to come out each night for a con-siderable period thereafter (when not inhibited by late cold spells) to feed. However, some do not do so every night. Some of my captive animals have not appeared at the surface with the others, even when conditions have seemed to be almost ideal. For example, I once had a single Couch's Spadefoot with the others in this container and saw it irregularly at various times of night. Then it disappeared and I did not see it for several months. I assumed that it had died underground and had practically forgotten it when, at 9 :30 p.m. one night a year later, there it was as healthy and plump as any of the others. It was larger than when I had last seen it which, of course, means that it must have come up, occasionally at least, to feed when I was not there, but that it should do so every night is quite unlikely since my visits to the container had occurred at various times of night up to 2 :00 a.m. This is an extreme case, perhaps, but I have also "lost" other specimens of other species in the same way with sufficient regularity to convince me that some individuals do not emerge from the ground when they might have been expected.

Furthermore, field observations give comparative evidence; for, after warm rains one finds considerably more animals active in nature than when there has been no rain, even when covering a smaller territory in a shorter time. This could not be consistently true if there were not more spadefoots above ground to be found. For those who know spadefoots, I must add that everything I have said here is not associated with the breeding urge which is discussed later and was kept in mind while interpreting the results here reported. These conclusions are also supported by Pearsons's studies of the Eastern Spadefoot and tend to confirm what he found.

In this matter of emergence *vs.* remaining in the burrow, the species of spadefoots seem to vary somewhat. Those in the Spea group (*hammondi, bombifrons,* and *intermontanus* at least) emerge more frequently than those of the other group (*holbrooki* and *hurteri*), with one known exception. Couch's Spadefoot behaves more like Hammond's or the Plains Spadefoot than like its closer relatives, in this and in other ways. The possible significance of this fact will be brought out in a later section.

It has long been emphasized that the Eastern Spadefoot may occupy a region for many years without ever being seen by man and many statements have been made implying that this animal may remain underground for more than a year—some have even said several years—without food, and there has been much "ohing" and "ahing" over this supposed fact, even by those who should know better. Worse yet, some, accepting this for what is often called *the* spadefoot, have extended the idea to other species (the Plains Spadefoot, for example) in which it is obviously and clearly not true (see, for example, Brooks, 1930). No animal can exist indefinitely without food and no spadefoot is equipped to feed below the surface of the ground. The spadefoots can and often do remain for long periods underground, but no individual of any species stays there alive for years at a time. What apparently happens is that rarely, if at all, do *all* the Eastern Spadefoots of a region emerge and feed during any given night (Pearson, 1955). Being secretive, protectively colored, almost completely nocturnal, and present at the surface locally in small numbers at any one time, they pass unnoticed until, suddenly, their loud, hoarse breeding call announces their presence in large numbers. The same is probably true of Hurter's Spadefoot, adults of which I have found active in nature only during and after rains despite my best efforts to find them at other times in central Oklahoma where I know the population to be large.

But the members of the Spea group (and Couch's Spadefoot, as well) often are out in large numbers when a long search reveals not a single specimen of the other types; at least this has been my experience in Oklahoma. But even here, individual Plains Spadefoots in captivity have not emerged every night. The difference between the habit-groups seems, therefore, to be one of degree rather than of kind. Which individuals will emerge and which will not must be under some sort of control, but its nature seems to be entirely unknown at present.

There is another phase of emergence of the adults to feed which I first noted among my captives. This is a marked tendency to leave the ground later each night as the season advances. During April and well into May, most individuals which were active on a given night emerged during twilight (or just after darkness in Hurter's Spadefoot). From late May through June, fewer were up in the early evening but more emerged from nine to eleven o'clock. By mid-August, not only fewer emerged each night but also those which did so seldom appeared until near midnight or even later. By mid-September, all had retreated for the winter.

For those who may wish to know the evidence for these statements, I offer the following. At various times when no spadefoots were at the surface (sundown to about midnight) I thoroughly stirred the top soil to obliterate the openings of all burrows. By examining the container early the next morning I could easily determine if the animals had emerged, and approximately how many had done so, by the presence and numbers of now open burrows. In addition, some of the specimens were marked so that I knew them individually and, by digging them out of the soil below an open burrow, could learn which had been active during my absence, since each animal tends to occupy a burrow alone.

This tendency for later seasonal emergence was also shown by several groups of juveniles of the Plains Spadefoot kept through the summer at my home. When tiny, these little fellows emerged from the soil at twilight and each fed until its stomach was full, then returned to its burrow. As they grew and the season advanced, they came out later and in fewer numbers until, in mid-August, their behavior was like that of adults in this respect. This could have been a reaction to increasing temperatures but not to decreased soil moisture, for water was added to the soil as it seemed to be needed. In September, wishing to retain some young spadefoots through the winter, I transferred them to my office and secured a supply of insects with which to feed them, supposing that in the warm room they would need and seek food. They returned to the soil and remained there as passive as they would have been during the coldest weather of winter out-of-doors and I could not induce them to eat insects even when I dug them out.

During the same winter, I confined adult Couch's Spadefoots in my office. They immediately burrowed and remained entirely passive despite the warm room. I dug out a few from time to time. Always these were found with eyes closed and it took some minutes to "awaken" them. When released they returned to the soil and remained there. Apparently none were voluntarily active until the morning of February 2. At eight a.m. that day a single male was out on the surface alert and with eyes open. This may have been due to my adding too much water or wetting the soil too frequently, since spadefoots are as "fussy" about too much as too little moisture.

In any case, all of this seems best interpreted on the theory of adaptive response to environment, now at least partly fixed in the hereditary patterns of the spadefoots. During their long evolution in essentially arid climates, natural selection worked *against* those individuals that came to the surface more often than necessary; and *for* those which did not do so (Bragg, 1961a). Spring, when the optimum conditions of temperature, moisture and food supply occur, is the most advantageous to them. As the heat of summer comes (especially in their desert home) a retreat below ground is the safest place, as it is also in winter when their food supply is limited, and sudden cold may envelope any large area with a continental type climate such as that of the Southwest. Such habits became firmly fixed in the hereditary pattern early in the evolutionary history of the spadefoots and were carried with them by this means as they spread out and became the different species known today. This apparently is why the Eastern Spadefoot seems to behave so peculiarly as compared to other amphibians occupying the same area.

III

Reproductive Activities

To survive in nature a species must, of course, have individuals that reproduce, and it must ordinarily do this in its natural environment. Terrestrial amphibians have a special problem in this, because most of them have not succeeded in evolving means of effective reproduction on land. The great majority of them, therefore, go to water courses, ponds or pools in their vicinity each year to produce the eggs that develop into aquatic larvae, which after a period of growth and development change to the adult form, leave the water, and grow into terrestrial adults. Since amphibians are like other vertebrates in having two sexes, both of which must take part in reproduction, there must be some regulatory mechanism controlling the behavior of each sex in order that they go to the proper waters at the same time. In the words of Bonner[1] for animals in general, "Unless egg and sperm can be ripe and in close proximity at all times, which would be a wasteful and unlikely situation, it is important to have a timing mechanism by which they can be brought together by both sexes when both are ripe."

[1] Bonner, 1958, *The Evolution of Development.* Cambridge University Press.

47

If males searched pools for females only in the fall but females occurred there only in springtime, no reproduction would be possible and the species would soon become extinct.

Vertebrates, as a whole, are known to have such a mechanism, differing in many details in the various groups, but characteristically involving three major factors : (1) the cycle of development of the sex-cells in both males and females which must in some way be synchronized in order that the two types of sex-cells will be ready simultaneously; (2) cyclic differential secretions of various hormones, particularly of the pituitary and sex glands, which in part, at least, control the first mentioned cycle; (3) reaction to environmental factors such as seasonal cycles in temperature, rainfall, light differences, length of day and many others. Just how these factors interact is only partly known for vertebrates as a whole and that which is known is so complex and diversified from group to group that a volume would scarcely suffice to give an adequate account of it.[2]

Many Amphibia, including several common frogs and toads, have the sex-cell and hormonal cycles physiologically synchronized on a seasonal basis. That is to say, they have a breeding *season* during which (and *only* during which) members of both sexes go to the water, cooperate to produce fertilized eggs, and then climb out and take up their other activities. They feed ravenously during the summer (especially true of the females) and a large part of the food taken is used to produce the next crop of sex-cells which are ready as the next breeding season approaches. Just when the season comes varies with species. The leopard frogs of my boyhood in Maine breed early in the spring as when I first found them, never in July or August. The bullfrog in the North breeds from late May

---

[2] For a good short résumé of this matter see Bullough, 1951. *Vertebrate Sexual Cycles,* Methuen and Co. Ltd., London, and John Wiley and Sons, Inc., New York City.

to early July. One little frog-like species in the South breeds
in winter or very early spring, never in summer or fall. The
Spring Peeper is so named because we hear its peeping breeding call in early springtime, not later. The emphasis here is
that each of these (and many others) has a breeding season
during which, and *only* during which, each normally does all
the breeding that is to occur during any one year. This is so
common a phenomenon among northeastern North American
and European Amphibia that many zoologists have written as
though *all* behave in this way. Let us see what might happen
if a spadefoot did so in its normal desert or grassland environment.

Suppose the breeding season to be in the early spring,
essentially March and April. At this season cold dry winds
commonly sweep over the habitat and all or most of the
streambeds and depressions have little or no water. If early
storms bring rain, the temperatures characteristically drop
suddenly below that optimum for spadefoot activity. Of
course, in a local situation, occasionally conditions might (and
probably would) be right for breeding but over the whole
region on a long-term basis there would be little opportunity
and a species which attempted breeding *only* then would be in
danger of extinction.

Suppose the breeding season to be late spring, essentially
May through June. In the desert and grassland climates, temperature would offer little difficulty to adults and locally
there are often heavy rains. It would seem that this would be
the best time of the whole year; and so it would be, but there
are further difficulties. The drier the climate, the less likelihood
there is of rainfall locally; and it is the local population of
any one place that breeds. If *all* were ready for reproduction
only at this time, production of eggs would be very spotty,
occuring only when and if it happened to rain enough in

any one place during the season. Any one population of spade-foots might build up during exceptionally rainy months of May and June but each would face the possibility of extinc-tion during long dry periods including these months, a com-mon phenomenon in dry deserts.

In similar manner, summer heat and winter cold (in addi-tion to dryness) would be a constant threat in these seasons, and autumn would seem to be little better. In fact, in the habitat of the primitive spadefoots where their reproductive habits developed, there is no time of the year in which posses-sion of a breeding season, in the sense that the leopard frogs of my boyhood have one, would be safe for them. This being true (with the further obvious fact that there are now plenty of individual spadefoots even in the desert and semidesert regions of the North American Southwest) indicates some sort of special adaptation to meet the situation, another one of the "makeshifts" of Romer.

The spadefoots, therefore, have no breeding season. Instead, they utilize the sudden appearance of water whenever and however it happens to come. Typically, this means that they breed only after rains, but they do this at almost any time when the temperature is not too low. There is no certainly known exception to this principle among the spadefoots, but there is one slight modification. The Great Basin Spadefoot often (and perhaps usually) utilizes the flood waters of streams overflowing valleys below mountains even when no rain occurs where it lives (Lindsdale, 1930). Also, Blair (1956) found them in permanent water and otherwise different from other spadefoots. But it is the sudden appearance of water in quan-tity that most spadefoots need, not rain as such. In the habitat of most spadefoots this normally comes only with rains.

Speaking of the Eastern Spadefoot, Gosner and Black (1955) summarize the basic facts thus :

"In the northeastern United States the breeding activities of most species [of frogs and toads] follow a seasonal pattern that is repeated with minor variations each spring. This type of behavior is contained in the concept of a mesic breeding behavior pattern (Bragg, 1945). In contrast, *S. h. holbrooki* illustrates the xeric breeding pattern including the following points of interest : 1) Heavy rainfall is the primary control in the initiation of breeding activity; 2) In the usual sense there is no definite breeding season, reproductive activity is spasmodic and unpredictable; 3) Transient pools are resorted to even when more permanent situations are available; 4) Potentially, embryonic and larval development proceeds at a very rapid rate."

These authors go on to point out that the Eastern Spadefoot shows considerable independence of environmental temperature, sometimes breeding with those forms having a breeding season in early spring, at other times with those breeding later in spring or summer. It is this erratic behaviour at breeding in any one place, together with its secretive, nocturnal habits as previously emphasized, which long made this animal so puzzling to the earlier biologists of the Northeast. Ball (1936) calls attention to the fact that this animal has not been noticed in New Haven, Connecticut, since a breeding congress was observed there by Smith in 1879. Yet Babbit (1932) found it in northern Connecticut and Ball himself reports it from several localities in this state. Emphasizing the scarcity of observations in the northern United States before he wrote, Ball says that only about sixteen times in one hundred and twenty five years have Eastern Spadefoots been reported in the regions approximately from Massachusetts through New Jersey. Yet there are still plenty of them to be found where local conditions are right for breeding, as shown recently by the studies of Gosner and Black in New Jersey, Dunn (1930) and Driver (1936) in Massachusetts, and by several observers farther south, e.g., Richmond (1947) in Virginia and Pearson (1955) and Neil (1957) in Florida.

Hanson (1958) summarized records of one hundred and forty five breeding congresses of the Eastern Spadefoot reported from August 15, 1834, to September 29, 1957, by forty-four biologists. It is interesting to note, parenthetically, that the first report of this spadefoot's call was published the year before the animal was named, at a time when no one knew that such a thing as a spadefoot existed. How puzzling and interesting such a sound must have been to those first hearing it! Hansen goes on to note that the average rainfall for forty-three of these breeding congresses was about 2.74 in., ranging from a low of 0.39 in. to a high of 8.0 in. Spadefoots do not usually breed after as little as under 0.5 in. of rain. The prime requisite, as stated earlier, seems usually to be exceptionally heavy rainfall locally or, in the Spea group particularly, its rate of fall (Bragg and Smith, 1942).

In the more typical spadefoot habitat in the Southwest, sudden and heavy rains are the rule rather than the exception, and the spadefoots breed more often. But here they are faced by another problem, the danger of a pool's drying up too quickly for the young to survive. They meet this in part by a great hurrying of their breeding as illustrated by some observations which I made on the development of a breeding congress of the Plains Spadefoot some years ago in central Oklahoma, as follows:

Two and one half inches of rain had fallen in about two hours, the sky clearing just before sundown. Air temperature was 15° C. at 8.00 p.m., just before complete darkness, when I heard the first voices in an extensively flooded field. At first I heard only a few calls; within ten minutes, at least twice as many animals were calling, and, by circling about the pool, I observed that a steady stream of spadefoots was coming in

from all directions to the breeding area. I caught and examined a good sample of these. All were males of a single
species, the Plains Spadefoot *(Scaphiopus bombifrons)*. These
males entered the pool as they reached it and soon were calling as lustily as those first there. Within an hour hundreds of
spadefoot males were bobbing like so many light balloons on
the pool's surface, each every second or less giving voice to a
single loud "Wah"!

At first, my wading about the pool flashing a light here and
there frightened the animals, some of which ducked under the
surface for protection. Later, after the full development of the
chorus, the animals paid no attention to my movements among
them until touched. Even then, touching them lightly under
the forelegs not only did not frighten them but actually stimulated them all the more. Each tried to clutch my fingers with
its front legs as though attempting to climb into my hand. (I
have actually stimulated calling garden toads, *Bufo,* to do this
and had them continue calling while sitting on my open palm
three feet above the water).

Circling the pool again after finding the first females in the
water at about 9.15, I found that a large number of spadefoots were still coming toward the pool. Sampling again proved
that most were males, some females. At 10.05, I found a
mated pair and, thereafter, several others, till observations were
discontinued at 2.00 a.m., at which time the chorus was still
in full swing and a few females, but no males, were noted
headed toward the water.

It had already been observed that breeding males move
about only incidentally while calling. Each essentially lies
sprawled on the surface and calls with little swimming about.
Just after midnight I saw how males of this species secure
females. My light picked up six spadefoots floating near the
center of the pool, five of which were calling lustily. The sixth

not only did no calling but moved slowly and steadily toward the calls. This was a female. She swam a few strokes, then paused motionless on the surface. Then she repeated this. Soon she was near one of the calling males. She approached slowly and eventually touched the male, which stopped calling and grabbed frantically at her. Both went under water but soon emerged at the surface as a mated pair, the male grasping the female with his forearms just in front of her hind legs, a mating position characteristic of spadefoots and a few other amphibians. Such pairs may be picked up and handled fairly roughly without the male releasing the female.

The next morning no spadefoots could be found in or about this pool at 9.15, but many of their eggs were present. These had been produced in small masses of jelly and left attached to grass and weeds at the edge and bottom of the pool. Each jelly mass (of several examined) contained from 6 to 110 eggs. Since it is known that each female produces several hundred eggs, it follows that a mated pair must move from place to place during the egg-laying process, producing a few eggs here and a few there on the vegetation available. Each such mass, therefore, represents only a fraction of the eggs laid by a single female.

On the second night, nearly as many males called here as on the first, but I found only a few females. On the third night a few males called but there was no large chorus and I saw no females. On the fourth night, I could find no evidence of spadefoot adults.

I have seen the essence of these observations during the breeding of *Scaphiopus bombifrons* literally hundreds of times during the past twenty years. The following generalizations seem to apply to this species:

1. Males, when stimulated by rainfall at the proper temperatures, precede females at a given time and site.

2.   Many more males are typically present than females at a given time and place.

3.   Nearly all females which reach a breeding site eventually are clasped by males and produce eggs.

4.   Many males, however, do not succeed in securing mates.

5.   Most, if not all, eggs that will be laid after a single rain are produced during the first night at any one site; unsuccessful males may call during the second night and a few even on the third. Under some conditions, one of these may secure a female but this is rare.

6.   Unless again stimulated by rainfall, males typically give up the breeding attempt after two or three nights without securing a female. If only weakly stimulated, as by a light rain, many males call only during one night anyway and some, at the border-line condition of stimulation, may not do so at all.

7.   Breeding congresses develop into huge numbers of males primarily because the calls of one male are stimulating to other males. The first rain-stimulated male to find a suitable pool enters and starts calling. Others of its species are attracted to the site by this sound. The louder the calls are, apparently, the more attractive to others within hearing. Similarly, females are attracted to the pools by the calls of the males, each female typically following the loudest clamoring (a few males in a pool often fail to secure females if other, louder choruses are nearby). It seems likely that a certain intensity of sound needs to be built up before females respond, but of this I am not quite sure. And, of course, the intensity of sound perceived by a given female depends, in part, on her proximity to a good pool containing calling males.

8.   Males secure females by attracting them rather than searching for them, even after both are in the water. If one

male happens to touch another (and this is common enough in a crowded breeding congress) each immediately behaves as though the other was a female. Since both are attempting to get into the typical clasping position, a struggle ensues which continues till one succeeds in this. Thereupon the clasped male utters a call and is immediately and violently released. From this it seems practically certain that sex recognition in these animals is primarily a matter of voice. Females do not need to recognize each other as females, since they do not clasp others. Female spadefoots have a voice, but I have never heard it in a breeding congress. It is the males only which do the sexual calling.

These details in the breeding pattern of the Plains Spadefoot are duplicated in many respects by other species, but there are also differences. The latter, while sometimes slight, I wish to emphasize because upon them often depend some quite basic differences in habitat and evolution. Let us, therefore, consider some of them.

1. *Difference in breeding sites.* The Plains Spadefoot and Hammond's Spadefoot, and possibly the Great Basin Spadefoot all typically use deeper pools or deeper parts of pools of varying depths when these are available (water one to three feet deep or deeper). In contrast, Hurter's Spadefoot and Couch's Spadefoot use water of a few inches to one foot in depth even when deep water is also available. However, all spadefoots in my experience will use any temporary water, deep or shallow, rather than not attempt to breed at all, and in water of inter-mediate depth, occasionally both types may breed (Bragg, 1962, 1963). I have studied many congresses of these species (except the Eastern Spadefoot, which I have never seen breed-ing) and have always found them behaving as though they had the preferences stated. What such apparent preference is based upon, I have no way of knowing, but it is evident that

it is one fairly effective barrier to the crossing of species. In Oklahoma, for example, three species may breed in the same region following violent rains. Two of these are "deep-water" species, the other a "shallow-water" form. I have found evidence of the crossing of the "deep-water" species in this region (as has Blair, 1955, elsewhere) but never of the "shallow-water" one with either of the others, although we learn from Dr. Wasserman's work that interbreeding is possible. Any method of sexual isolation is involved in the mechanism of evolution and is important to students of speciation.

2. *Differences in methods of securing females by males.* *Scaphiopus hammondi* and *Scaphiopus holbrooki hurteri* commonly call from the surface just as *Scaphiopus bombifrons* was described above to do. However, instead of remaining in one place and attracting a female by voice alone, these males swim actively while calling and attempt to clasp any spadefoot which comes near. Of the two, males of Hammond's spadefoot are the more active in this. Two males of the latter species often rush at each other and wrestle on the surface till one gets the clasping position on the other. A croak from the one beneath, in my experience, however, always has resulted in its release by the one above. Couch's Spadefoot does this also, but in this species males sometimes call from the shore and attack other individuals entering the pool (Ortenburger, 1924). Males so caught are released immediately as in other species, but females are retained tenaciously, the pair entering the water for egg-laying. Since Couch's Spadefoot is a "shallow-water" form, and other species likely in most places to breed in the same region are "deep-water" forms, crossing is not likely to occur. Such barriers to interbreeding are often called isolating mechanisms.

In the Plains Spadefoot, as observed in central and western Oklahoma, breeding does not occur below about 52° F.

(9–10° C.) air temperature, but if rain in sufficient amount or violence falls below this temperature and the weather warms sufficiently during the next few days, the animals may go to the pools and breed (Bragg and Smith, 1948). Recent evidence of this has also been found for Hurter's Spadefoot as well (Bragg, 1959), and Gosner and Black's study of the Eastern Spadefoot suggests it for this species. Ball (1936) thought that the eastern form may breed at temperatures from as low as from 7.6–8.6° C. upward while Gosner and Black give 9.6° C. as the lowest in their experience. The latter compares well with my own estimate of 9–10° C. for *Scaphiopus bombifrons* in Oklahoma.

If we recall the physiological and germ-cell cycles in vertebrates mentioned earlier, we see further evidence of peculiarities in the spadefoots. It has been abundantly demonstrated that egg production in the female and sperm production in the male of several kinds of frogs and toads (including spadefoots) can be artificially stimulated by the hormones of the pituitary gland, and there is reason to believe that these hormones are always involved under natural conditions. If this be true for the spadefoots (very probable, but not known *certainly*), it seems to follow that rainfall must stimulate this gland to action or be involved in some mechanism which does so. As one of my former colleagues facetiously remarked, "How does the pituitary know when it rains?"

For the spadefoots and other species of the grasslands having a xeric pattern of breeding dependent on rainfall, I have suggested the following possibility (Bragg, 1941)—Rainfall may stimulate the nervous system of the male. This acts on the pituitary and together with its influence causes the male to seek a pool. Finding one stimulates calling which attracts the female. The clasp of the male on the female stimulates her pituitary through nervous action and this causes the release of eggs in the ovary. The eggs are thus laid and fertilized. It should be emphasized that this hypothesis has not been thoroughly checked as yet and, therefore, may not be correct. One bit of evidence for the function of the male in stimulating the female pituitary is that females almost never produce eggs unless they have been clasped for some time by males. This seems to be true of all species having the xeric pattern of breeding, whether spadefoots or not, but is known *not* to be so for several frogs and toads having a definite breeding season (i.e. having what I have called the mesic breeding pattern). In these, the pituitary function in stimulation of the release of eggs from the ovary often occurs without even the presence of the male and it may do so before clasping has occurred, even when males and females are together. It is possible also that ovulation in the xeric species is affected by the stimulating effect of the voice of the male.

Since the above was written, a new suggestion has been made by Hansen (1958). Working with Eastern Spadefoots, he found that females may carry eggs throughout the year. He also noted that uptake of water by the body of the animal created a tonicity not present otherwise, and he thinks that this may be the factor which stimulates the pituitary of the female and thus causes the release of eggs from the ovary. He also says that males need water intake for sperm release.

This hypothesis is certainly as reasonable as my own and has the added advantage of some experimental evidence to support it. But we still need more critical observations. Why, under either hypothesis, should some females respond to the males and others not at a given time and place, especially if they have eggs ready for release? Both Hansen and I have observed this but neither of us has offered a satisfactory explanation.

Whatever the details may be, male spadefoots find temporary pools quickly during and after rains and some females join them about as fast as is possible after they begin calling. The breeding call differs in each species. It is in all of them a single hoarse grinding note, loud and penetrating, repeated at intervals of a second or less, mostly while the male floats on the surface of the water. Two or three hundred males in one pool make such a racket that they can often be heard for one or two miles on a still night. Males of some spadefoots may call from the bank as well as from the surface of the water and intercept females as they arrive at the pool as earlier indicated, but the characteristic calling position is the floating one.

Each male has an inflatable vocal sac under its chin which acts as a resonance chamber to increase the volume of sound. Air is forced from the lungs through the larynx and this vibrates the vocal cords (or nerve action may stimulate the movement of the cords against the air current, as has been recently suggested). It then inflates the vocal sac and returns to the lungs at the end of each call. The mouth remains closed. As each call is made by a floating spadefoot, the sudden expansion of the large resonance sac is accompanied by a backward movement of the head and the animal's back is depressed. In some males which I have watched calling I have suspected a voluntary movement of the head backward to accommodate the expansion of the sac.

Most temporary pools in which I have studied spadefoot breeding have been quite turbid and, consequently, I have never seen their actual egg-laying process in nature. The eggs are known to be fertilized outside the body of the female and, since they are found later in small masses attached to vegetation below the water surface, it must follow, as stated earlier, that a pair moves about leaving some eggs here, some there, wherever suitable supports are found. Each pair produces several hundred eggs, the number varying with individuals and with species.

The eggs are small spheres, embedded in protective masses of jelly. The gelatinous envelopes are produced by the absorption of water by a muco-protein secreted by the oviducts about the eggs before they are laid. The jelly is soft but tough and elastic, and its surface is somewhat sticky so that it often picks up soil particles or other materials floating in the water, sometimes so many as to make a complete camouflage for the eggs. In two species jelly stalks have been found (once in each) by which each egg was attached to some object. Ortenburger (1924) found this in *Scaphiopus hammondi hammondi* in Arizona and I (Bragg, 1941a) in *Scaphiopus bombifrons* in New Mexico. This is not the usual thing in either species.

The color of the eggs and the appearance of the individual egg-masses vary with the species groups. The eggs of Spea (*Scaphiopus bombifrons* and *Scaphiopus hammondi* at least, for I have never seen the eggs of the Mexican Spadefoot) are brown or brownish gray above, shading to white below. Those of the other group (*Scaphiopus couchi Scaphiopus hurteri* and *Scaphiopus holbrooki holbrooki*) are very dark above and white below. These darker eggs typically occur in larger masses than the lighter ones of the Spea types.

Couch's Spadefoot commonly covers grass blades or plant stems with symmetrical cylinders of eggs and their jellies from near the bottom to near the surface of the water. Hurter's Spadefoot usually places a loose lattice-work of eggs draped over twigs or partly submerged vegetation, and Couch's Spadefoot often does the same. But the exact detail of egg production varies widely with conditions. I recently found eggs of Hurter's Spadefoot scattered singly or in small groups on the bottom of a pool that had nothing which could be used for egg supports (Bragg, 1957a). It would seem from this finding that some spadefoots, at least, are flexible in behavior, using supports for eggs or not as they are available. Since the eggs with stalks found by me were in very shallow water (Fig. 9), it may be that this variation is associated with shallow water.

IV

Larval Development and Behavior

The pools utilized by spadefoots in laying their eggs are typically temporary, recently formed and usually shallow ones. In general, the Spea group uses deeper water than do the others, but all species use very shallow water at times, and two basic biological problems face the developmental stages. They must secure food and they must do this in sufficient quantity to develop rapidly enough to be able to leave the pool before all water disappears. (See Figs. 16 and 17.)

In deserts and dry grasslands, both problems are severe ones. Depressions, when dry for months at a time and then suddenly filled by heavy or violent rainfall, are singularly barren places, sometimes with little organic matter in them. Being shallow, though often quite extensive, they present a large surface in relation to their volume to evaporation, which in hot weather and high winds is sometimes remarkably rapid. I have seen quite extensive flood waters evaporate within a week or two even in central Oklahoma, although conditions vary so much that no general statement is possible. In one exceptional pool in which I studied spadefoot development for about eleven years, conditions changed gradually from

63

one very good to one very poor for the spadefoots. In rainy years, seepage from a sandy hill above it at first about balanced the loss from evaporation and seepage from the pool, so that water remained longer than the spadefoots needed it. Algae and other aquatic plants thrived, and the spadefoot larvae had no trouble with the physical environment. Then a three-year drought came; water was not stored in the hill, there was no seepage into the pool, and very few spadefoot larvae had time to emerge. Food was scarce and water loss so rapid that often no tadpoles survived to inhabit the land. On the average the dangers to the young in such places necessitate special embryonic and larval adaptations, and these the young spadefoots have developed in marked degree.

The first to be noted is a very rapid developmental rate. At usual temperatures, the eggs hatch in about two days as contrasted with those of frogs, which may take nearly a week in the same water. For about another day the young tadpoles do nothing while awaiting the development of the mouth parts. By the time the mouth is functional, the food materials stored in the eggs by the mother spadefoot are gone and the tadpoles begin searching for food. This usually happens during the third day from egg-laying, but it may be delayed somewhat if the water happens to be cold or occur during the second day in exceptionally warm pools.

The tadpoles of spadefoots are neither quick moving nor fast swimmers at any stage, but they usually move almost continuously, pausing with slowly waving tails here and there to feed as things appealing to them may be found. In the Eastern Spadefoot and Hurter's Spadefoot, there is a marked tendency for the very young larvae to swim continuously near the surface, each sweeping back and forth seemingly aimlessly. Collectively they seem to sample every part of the surface water of the pool. During their first day of such action, they may double in size. They must be securing food in abundance but what it could be was long a mystery. Working with the Eastern Spadefoot in Virginia, Richmond (1947) finally proved that this form feeds upon minute organisms strained from the water, i.e., they are planktonic feeders during their first few days.

Since the closely related Hurter's Spadefoot often also behaves in this manner, I attempted to determine the type of organisms present as food objects. But, surprisingly, I found almost nothing in the water except bacteria in the particular pool examined. Then I noted that many of the spadefoot tadpoles here were not moving near the surface (although some were) but, instead, tended to mass in the shallow areas where they were vigorously gnawing at plant stems, leaves, and the bottom mud. In another pool nearby there were no leaves or other plant parts available and all the spadefoot tadpoles here were vigorously scooping up the bottom mud. They were so active in this that a steady stream of the materials of the pool's bottom was passing through them, and they were growing rapidly. Since minute plants (algae) are common on the bottom mud of some pools, I supposed that here the tadpoles were feeding upon such plants. A thorough microscopic examination of both the surface materials of the pool's bottom and the intestinal contents of some of the tadpoles revealed no such plants, however, but only an amorphous mass of organic material mixed with scattered bacteria and inorganic substances. I concluded that in this pool the tadpoles were scavengers, gobbling up the bottom mud and utilizing any organic matter in it which they could digest. I have since seen this phenomenon many times.

What tadpoles of Hurter's Spadefoot eat during their first few days, therefore, depends almost entirely upon the nature of the pool in which they hatch. In pools having planktonic organisms in abundance (a rare condition in my experience, but known in a few places), they are planktonic feeders like their eastern relatives. Where plankton is absent or scarce, they turn to almost any organic source available to them. In either case, they are very adept in finding and utilizing the organic materials present.

I have also studied this matter experimentally in the laboratory. Tadpoles of Hurter's Spadefoot which had never fed have been offered many food sources, including the bottom mud of various and numerous pools. In some such cultures they thrive; in others, waste away and die. Usually, however, about 5% to 10% eventually emerge through eating their dead fellows.

There is also evidence that members of Spea with which I am personally familiar (Hammond's Spadefoot and the Plains Spadefoot) are planktonic feeders. These, from their first feeding, also eat any organic materials which they can find, along plant stems or on the bottom. In barren pools the Plains Spadefoot, at least, also takes in large quantities of bottom mud, utilizing from it whatever is digestable. These also are predacious on small creatures. I know nothing about the early food of the tadpoles of other members of this group. As far as I know no one has studied the matter in these forms.

Very early in their lives as tadpoles, the spadefoots become very fond of meat. They will swarm upon pieces of beef or liver placed in the water or vigorously attack dead earthworms or dead, soft-bodied insect larvae. If a tadpole dies, it is immediately eaten by the others. Tadpoles of Hurter's Spadefoot have attacked my bare feet, thrust into a pool, so vigorously as to give me an unpleasant tickling and I have also induced them to gnaw at my fingers. I have recently succeeded also in getting much larger tadpoles of the Plains Spadefoot to do this.

The fast developmental rate of the embryonic stages of the Plains Spadefoot (Trowbridge and Trowbridge, 1937; M. S. Trowbridge, 1941, 1942) applies also to Hurter's and Couch's spadefoot (as I myself have found) and apparently also to the Eastern Spadefoot (Gosner and Black, 1955). This continues into the larval stages, but with interesting variations, at least in Hurter's Spadefoot in central Oklahoma, where I have studied them for many years. For example, several years ago tadpoles of Hurter's Spadefoot were produced in two adjacent pools. One of these, which we may call the upper pool, was a small ditch behind an old terrace in a pasture (Fig. 5). The other, a flat, broad ditch beside a highway, was a few rods down slope from the first. Eggs in each were laid on the same night and tadpoles hatched in them on the same day. In each pool the temperature fluctuated from day to day but at any one time seemed comparable. But since the lower pool was more extensive and shallow, total evaporation from it was faster than from the upper one. In a week, the tadpoles in the upper pool were half-again as large as in the lower one, and they continued to grow faster till they metamorphosed successfully at about four weeks of age. In the meantime, the tadpoles in the lower pool were killed by the total evaporation of the water when about three weeks from eggs.

The next year almost exactly this same thing happened, the tadpoles in the lower pool being killed when about fifteen to sixteen days from the egg stage, whereas those of the same age and of larger size in the upper pool went on to metamorphosis later. The third year, the cycle started in the same way, and since I now expected those in the lower pool to die as the water disappeared, I paid them less attention than those in the upper pool, although I saw them briefly each day.

On the 12th day after the eggs were laid, I visited these pools in the early evening. In the lower pool, only a small puddle remained in which there was a dense mass of tadpoles and the conditions were such that I fully expected the animals to die before morning. Visiting the area about 9.00 a.m. the following day, I found, as expected, no standing water in the lower pool. But I could find no dead tadpoles either! Investigation showed that all had transformed during the night and were now little toads each about as large as a house fly with some even smaller, all piled together under masses of moist, dead leaves at one end of the former pool. In the upper pool, larger tadpoles of the same age had not transformed, and they did not do so for about another week (Bragg, 1948, 1950d).

Why could the tadpoles in the lower pool transform in twelve to thirteen days this third year (which represents the fastest reported developmental rate among aquatic larval Amphibia) if older ones during the two previous years had failed to do so and had died as the water disappeared? It was not likely to be the effect of temperature, because, if so, the tadpoles in the upper pool should have emerged, since the temperatures in the two places had remained comparable. This seemed especially true since those in the upper pool were larger and therefore must have been better fed, since they were of the same age. Obviously something had increased the rate of development of those in the lower pool, enabling the animals to get out of the water sooner and at a much smaller size than usual without a corresponding increase in the rate of growth. I wanted to know what this factor was.

Consideration of all of the observations made here during the three-year period suggested only one cause, and this at the time seemed quite unlikely—the presence of dead tadpoles of the previous years (or, more exactly, chemicals derived from their presence in the dried mud between evaporation cycles in the pool). Since the tadpoles at this site during all three of these years had fed almost exclusively on the bottom mud, the possibility needed checking.

I did this experimentally and found that the presence of dead tadpoles (either of this or different species) did indeed stimulate the developmental rate. This was true both under experimental laboratory conditions (Bragg, 1950d) and in nature (Bragg, 1957b). My conclusions were that the rate of development and sometimes (but not always) the rate of growth were enhanced markedly by the enrichment of the bottom mud used as food by scavenging tadpoles of Hurter's Spadefoot, and that this enrichment consisted of something in or derived from the dead tadpoles there. I did not ascertain whether a special substance concentrated in their bodies was the cause or whether they merely added to the general food supply. I strongly suspect the former, however, for two reasons: (1) general conditions of nutrition as indicated by growth rates were better in the upper pool in all three years than in the lower, yet it was those in the lower pool which showed an increase in developmental rate in the third year. (2) Substances are known (e.g., iodine or thyroxin) that regulate the time of metamorphosis of tadpoles, which is, in part at least, under hormonal control. These (or similar substances) could well have been concentrated in the dead tadpoles in sufficient quantities to affect the larvae of the third generation.

In any event since, as we have already observed, nature tends to conserve the species rather than the individual, tadpoles of Hurter's Spadefoot which die through desiccation may still serve their species through the utilization of their bodies or substances derived from them by oncoming generations in quickly disappearing pools of poor nutritional quality. This phenomenon is so far known only for this one spadefoot.

Very recently phenomena closely related to the above have been found (Bragg, 1962, 1963). Some tadpoles of *Scaphiopus bombifrons* are predacious on other types of tadpoles (including those of *Scaphiopus couchi*). Those which show this both develop and grow very much faster than those in the same water which do not. This is also true of cannibalistic tadpoles (see beyond).

Other surprising adaptive phenomena have also shown up in tadpoles of some of the spadefoot species. One of these involves cooperative feeding at certain times and places. Abbott (1884) was apparently the first to observe this, although it was Richmond (1947) many years later who explained its meaning. Both were working with tadpoles of the Eastern Spadefoot. It seems, however, to be a general rule in spadefoots, for I have observed the same phenomenon in Hurter's, Couch's, and the Plains spadefoots, in the first one many times, in the second once, and in the third on several occasions.

The phenomenon usually consists of social feeding aggregations during which hundreds or thousands of tadpoles move as a cooperative unit through a pool, each beating its tail faster than seems necessary for its rate of forward movement. When such a mass of tadpoles moves along the bottom, the collective effect of the coordinated action of so many moving tails stirs up the bottom so that a stream of particles moves backward through the group. Each tadpole collects what it can of these particles, the remainder of the material passing out as a cloud behind the school. Sometimes, at least in Hurter's Spadefoot, there is little if any actual forward movement, the mass of animals stirring up materials in one place for a considerable time before moving on. In pools containing small floating or weakly swimming organisms (plankton) some schools apparently feed on planktonic organisms by pulling them through the mass of tadpoles instead of, or in addition to, materials from the bottom. In any case, each tadpole cooperates with all others in such a group to the nutritive benefit of all. I interpret such cooperative actions as social behavior.

Some very recent observations on the formation of *asocial* feeding aggregations of tadpoles of the Plains Spadefoot by the late Prof. Otis M. King and myself are of interest (Bragg and King, 1960). In a pool containing thousands of these tadpoles, slowly coursing about and feeding on the bottom, we noted a single large mass in mid-pool with the individuals moving much more swiftly from the bottom to the surface than others not so aggregated. This was obviously a feeding aggregation, but of a type slightly different from any ever seen before because the forward movement was very slow, the mass merely drifting about with the boiling mass of tadpoles stirring up the bottom mud by their collective movements and presumably feeding upon the materials so stirred. Except for these details, this looked like social cooperation in feeding, in principal like that already seen in the Eastern and Hurter's Spadefoots.

We investigated the matter further, however, and found this to be *asocial* behavior. When the bottom was disturbed under the non-aggregated tadpoles, a few nearby became greatly agitated, ramming their heads into the disturbed area. These were joined by more and more till a boiling mass of tadpoles had formed, essentially like the one first seen. Four such aggregations formed and "drifted" out into deeper water, eventually merging into one big mass. What had happened, obviously, was that the scarce food on the bottom had largely been used up, but there was more beneath the upper layer. When this was disturbed, more food substance was exposed. The first tadpoles to find this went after it, and others joined them. Thus, through their violent movements, they stirred the bottom further and exposed more food. There was no real cooperation here. Each tadpole was merely getting what food it could from the stirred bottom. The collective effect, however, was the same as in truly cooperative (i.e. social) feeding, as seen in *Scaphiopus holbrooki hurteri.*

One very puzzling thing is that the formation of social feeding aggregations are sporadic in occurrence. Such groups may form in a given pool, break down, and reform at the same time that other tadpoles continue to feed nearby without entering such aggregations, but at any time such individually feeding tadpoles may join a group moving by them. Occasionally, tadpoles are in looser aggregation with stragglers at the sides which may wander away individually at any time. In some pools Hurter's Spadefoot larvae may never form such aggregations. In others, few may occur outside them after the first few days. In still other pools great feeding aggregations may be present one day and none the next. No one yet knows why.

Such cooperative schools, whatever their cause, are adaptive in two ways : (1) through securing on the average more of the scarce food for each individual than it could usually find alone and thus helping in the severe "race" with evaporation to get to metamorphic size and/or stage of development before the water is gone, and (2) protection from the predatory attacks of beetle larvae.

The latter is not well understood and is based upon a few observations only, as follows. The larvae of the larger water beetles have long been known to eat tadpoles. I have watched those of the water scavenger beetles (*Hydrus triangularis*) catch and kill tadpoles of Hurter's Spadefoot on many occasions. Once while I was studying aggregations of these tadpoles in the upper pool mentioned above, I noted about six or seven of these beetle larvae converging toward a feeding school of tadpoles and was interested to determine whether their concerted attack on individuals in the school would frighten the tadpoles into scattering. But the bettle larvae never reached the mass of swimming spadefoots! As each came close, it veered off and swam along parallel to the school and each of several finally captured a tadpole well out of the aggregation. Since I made this observation several years ago, I have used every opportunity in my study of these tadpoles to note the relation of feeding aggregations to the predatory attacks of these beetle larvae and I have never yet seen one of these enter a tadpole aggregation. Since they readily attack an individual not in an aggregation, there must be some influence from the grouping which inhibits the beetles; but none know what this is. There are several possibilities which readily come to mind. Among these are: (1) avoidance of local concentration of carbon dioxide presumably present in and about the aggregation caused by the respiratory activities of the tadpoles; (2) avoidance of slightly higher concentration of the hydrogen ion from the same cause; (3) production of obnoxious secretions in sufficient quantity by the tadpoles when present *en masse* but not sufficiently otherwise; (4) reaction to currents in the water caused by the moving tails of the tadpoles. All of these hypotheses and many others need experimental checking.

Other adaptations to life in transient pools shown by the spadefoot tadpoles involve another kind of social behavior. This has been seen several times in each of two species, Hurter's Spadefoot and the Plains Spadefoot. I have called the phenomenon the formation of scooping aggregations (Bragg, 1959).

As the water level in a pool becomes very low (and only then, as far as has ever been seen) small groups of tadpoles gather on the bottom, usually stop feeding, and move their tails in such a way that a depression is formed in the mud of the pool's bottom. The tail movements are not particularly vigorous, but often the collective effect is sufficient to roil slightly the water in the immediate vicinity. The width of the depression so formed will vary with the size of the aggregation of tadpoles forming it and its depth with the length of time that the scooping action continues. In some pools, two or three groups of various sizes may be working at the same time that other tadpoles are continuing to feed, either individually or in feeding aggregations. I do not recall ever seeing all the spadefoot tadpoles in a single pool in one scooping aggregation, and usually only a hundred or two of the thousands present are in such groups at any given time and place.

No one understands the cause of such action, especially (1) why all tadpoles in the same pool do not behave in any one way at a given time and (2) why scooping aggregations do not always occur as water loss from the pool becomes severe. But that scooping aggregations are adaptive to a special situation seems clear enough. Its function is to cut down the rate of evaporation through lessening the amount of surface exposed to the action of sun and wind. Such reduction in total evaporation as the water level becomes dangerously low often gives sufficient time for the tadpoles to get ready for metamorphosis before all are killed by desiccation. Many times I have seen many or, more rarely, all of the tadpoles in a given pool save their lives in this way. For example, tadpoles of Hurter's Spadefoot of the same age and of comparable sizes in two adjacent and apparently similar pools were about midway in their development. As the water became low in each through evaporation, several scooping aggregations were formed in one pool but not in the other. In the first, as the water level rapidly fell, the last puddles lay in the depressions formed by the aggregations, and from these the tadpoles transformed just as the water was gone. In the second pool, all the tadpoles died and all surface water disappeared about four hours before it had left the depressions formed by the tadpoles in the first pool. The time saved by the work of the scooping aggregations in forming the depressions had made all the difference in the world to these two lots of tadpoles.

Still a third type of social aggregation has been seen in spadefoot tadpoles. I first saw this in 1941 and described it in the paper (Bragg, 1944) which gave the first account of the tadpoles of Hurter's Spadefoot, at that time wholly unknown. Since then I have seen it many times in many different kinds of pools in central Oklahoma and have shown it to colleagues and friends; but still its significance is not very clear. It so far is certainly known only in Hurter's and Couch's Spadefoots but probably occurs also in the eastern form, and I have twice seen something like it in the Plains Spadefoot.

As the tadpoles of Hurter's Spadefoot approach metamorphic size and/or age, their coloration changes and whitish curved stripes appear on the back suggestive of the adult pattern. Meanwhile, the almost black ground color characteristically becomes lighter, usually some shade of brown. Occasionally, darker brownish stripes occur on a lighter brown background. In pools where the water is clear, the coloration is generally darker than in turbid pools (Bragg, 1957c). As these changes occur, hind-limb buds, present but small during the earlier stages, enlarge rapidly and differentiate into perfect hind legs with joints at hip, knee, and ankle and with fully formed toes. Forelimbs are also forming but do not yet appear on the outside, since they now are still enclosed in the respiratory chamber which all tadpoles form about the gill-region soon after hatching. The tail is still perfect and, whereas the hind legs can be moved at will, they are not yet normally used. These external changes are manifestations of the earlier phases of the impending emergence to the land as juvenile spadefoots.

At this stage, either just before the forelegs emerge through the body wall or just after, the tadpoles may or may not form metamorphic aggregations. If they do not, then each, when ready, approaches the bank, crawls out, usually finds some object to crawl under and remains quiet while completing its transformation. This is a very rapid process in most spadefoots. Within a half hour, the tail is already shriveled and is being absorbed rapidly, the mouth is much enlarged, the larval teeth and horny jaws are lost (this often happens even before leaving the water) and marked internal changes have occurred. Within three to five hours, the tadpole has become essentially a little toad, the tail region only a tiny stub, and the animal is now prepared to take up the life on land.

These bodily changes occur in the same manner whether metamorphic aggregations are formed or not, and the time relationships are comparable. The difference, therefore, is wholly in behavior during the process. If such aggregations do occur, this is what happens. At the stage just before or just after the forelegs appear, groups of tadpoles become aggregated into large masses, often containing thousands of individuals, although some groups are smaller. These aggregations usually occur on or near the bottom of the pool if the water is low, but close in at the shoreline if not. Tadpoles in them usually do not feed, although in some cases recently seen, a few were doing so as typical feeding aggregations were changing into metamorphic aggregations. In a fully formed aggregation of this type, the tadpoles are in continuous movement, milling about like peas in a boiling pot. They leave the aggregation only to come to the surface to gulp air as each needs to do so but each returns immediately to the swarming mass below. At the edges of the mass, a tadpole which happens to be forced outward or which swims to the edge never continues its movement away; unless frightened, it always turns and re-enters the aggregation.

Such behavior often continues for hours in one small part

of the pool because, typically, such masses do not move much from place to place. These are not schools, if by this is meant that the animals move together, with apparent purpose, from one place to another. However, the random movement of the whole seething mass sometimes forces it against objects such as sedge clumps or other plants so that such a group may become divided, more or less mechanically, into two or more groups. Also, if two such aggregations are close together, the mechanical motions of each may cause the two masses to "drift" closer to each other, and, if they approach each other closely enough, they may merge into a single larger aggregation.

If one thrusts an object into such an aggregation, tadpoles in it react by scattering wildly in all directions, obviously through fear. As soon as the disturbance is over, new aggregations form, and within ten or fifteen minutes all is as before except that now there are usually several smaller groups composed of the individuals which made up the larger aggregation before its disturbance. (This, incidently, also happens often in disturbance of feeding aggregations.) These new aggregations may remain small or unite with others nearby as already explained.

In typical cases (some exceptions are mentioned below) tadpoles in metamorphic aggregations maintain this behavior for several hours and then, just as darkness falls, all or nearly all of the several hundreds or thousands in each aggregation move almost simultaneously to the bank, crawl out *en masse,* and seek shelter under leaves or other objects while they complete their transformation. Since the adults, which these young are in the process of becoming, are almost strictly nocturnal, this behavior strongly suggests a reaction to the fading light as the twilight deepens. This is especially so, since many animals of very diverse groups are known to react positively or negatively to different light intensities and spadefoots are exactly the kind of animal that one would expect to do this.

But, here again, the spadefoots surprise and puzzle us. Sometimes, as already stated, the tadpoles do not form metamorphic aggregations, although, if some so perform in a given pool, usually they all do so. But still more inexplicable are cases wherein things progress as expected, metamorphic aggregations form in the typical manner, and then the tadpoles start emerging to the bank *without* waiting for the fading light. Also, in many cases they do not move out of the water simultaneously as expected from conditions described above as typical, but each goes to the bank from an aggregation whenever it feels the urge to do so. Superficially, all in an aggregation may appear in the same stage but they emerge from the water individually, day or night, through a period of several hours.

In one pool in the spring of 1954 I saw quite exceptional behavior involving metamorphic aggregations (Bragg, 1957b). The groups formed normally and at the stage expected. Then, as I was watching the behavior of the animals, typical so far, suddenly a large aggregation broke down completely with tadpoles swimming fast in all directions, but slightly more slowly than when artifically disturbed. Soon, small groups were coming together on the bottom, these merging with other small groups, until, in about 20 minutes a large aggregation had built up. A few minutes later this group also "exploded" with tadpoles swimming rapidly in all directions. Soon again they re-formed an aggregation. I was at this pool several times during the next twenty-four hours. This behavior continued with minor modifications for long periods. Occasionally only one side of the aggregation broke down in this way and sometimes two or more aggregations were re-formed instead of one.

I looked very carefully for any stimulus which might have

affected the animals but could find none either within the water or outside it. So far as I could tell it was a sudden, spontaneous movement, as though one tadpole acted as a leader, the others following, similar to what one often sees in wheeling flocks of flying birds or in some of the movements in schools of fishes. But, since this occurred in a single pool and the behavior was different from that observed dozens of times elsewhere, there may have been special stimulating factors here that were unrecognized. So, again, we must await further opportunities to study this in greater detail before we can be sure of anything other than the behavior itself.

These same metamorphic aggregations were exceptional in two other ways. As the time approached for them to emerge to the shore, all the tadpoles were in one huge aggregation at the shallower, eastern end of the long, narrow pool. Suddenly the whole aggregation started moving, forming a long dense school headed westward, just off the shore from the northern bank. The movements were indistinguishable from those in a feeding aggregation, and the rate of locomotion was about the same. But there was no feeding. As the school progressed, two or three, then others (singly or in small groups) left the mass and crawled out onto the bank to finish their transformation in the regular manner. By the time the school had progressed two-thirds of the distance (about 100 feet) to the other end of the pool, fully half had left it for the shore. This resulted, of course, in the spreading of little spadefoots all along the north bank, approximately equally spaced. By the next morning they had completely transformed and wandered away from the pool. Only this once have I ever observed schooling movements of a metamorphic aggregation and only this once seen emergence of this type. Again, I do not know why. Twice since then, tadpoles have hatched in this pool, but have disappeared inexplicably within a few days. Road building has recently disturbed this breeding site so that further study there is impossible.

In the recent study of Spadefoot tadpoles by Professor King and myself noted earlier, we also saw a type of *social* aggregation among the tadpoles in another pool which does not fit into the classification of types of aggregations earlier given. All of thousands present here were in aggregations with individuals in any one school all closely packed together and headed in the same direction. They moved very slowly, each feeding from the bottom with no stirring of materials that we could see, very different from the boiling schools seen in an adjacent pool. These were basically feeding schools, but with a difference! Many of these schools were headed into the shore, and, on nearing it, individual tadpoles forged ahead, forcing their way to the front and then climbing out onto the bank as metamorphosing individuals. In a crescent-shaped region near each such school (immediately on shore in front of it), hundreds of juvenile spadefoots hopped about or had formed tiny burrows, some individuals with their heads protruding from them.

This then, was something like a metamorphic aggregation as seen in *Scaphiopus holbrooki hurteri*, but differed from it in that the majority of the animals were still feeding and also in that the tadpoles in each group were oriented as in a feeding school. The species involved was *Scaphiopus bombifrons*.

Scientists are noted for their skepticism and there is good reason why this should be so. Human proclivity for error is so well recognized that unexpected observations (and, especially, interpretations of these) are, and should be, questioned if there seems to be any reason for question, especially if unconfirmed by others.

Aggregational phenomena in spadefoot tadpoles have actually been reported by only a few individuals who had the interest and opportunity to observe them. Feeding schools were apparently first seen but not fully understood by Abbott (1884) and Ball (1936), and they were certainly seen by Richmond (1947), all working with the Eastern Spadefoot. I have observed them in three species (Hurter's, Couch's, and the Plains Spadefoot). But scooping aggregations, while reported in two species (Hurter's and the Plains Spadefoot) and seen several times by me, are not yet confirmed by reports of other workers. Similarly, true metamorphic aggregations have been described only in Hurter's, Couch's, and the Plains Spadefoots and only by me and, hence, need the confirmatory observations of others. I also seem to be the only one to have reported mass movements by tadpoles from a pool, although such movements of juveniles, after metamorphosis, have been observed on several occasions (see Neil, 1957, and my comment on this paper, Bragg, 1958).

Richmond's study was the first to demonstrate planktonic feeding in any spadefoot tadpole and he very properly questioned whether what I had called metamorphic aggregations might not be feeding schools imperfectly observed. He might well have been right, since I assumed in the earlier phases of my studies that these tadpoles feed only on substantially visible materials as most tadpoles do. However, observations since that time have demonstrated to my complete satisfaction that the two phenomena are basically different, as already detailed above. However, the recently found type of asocial aggregation in the Plains Spadefoot needs further study. I hope that the desirable confirmation of my observations will soon be made to check the obvious possibility that I may be, at least in part, in error. As will be shown immediately, I can make mistakes.

CANNIBALISM :

Mention was made earlier of the meat-eating proclivities of spadefoot tadpoles. It should be noted that tadpoles of most of the common frogs and toads occasionally eat meat as available, and that many of them will eat dead larvae of their own kind. Thus they may be said to be cannibalistic at times. Occasional real predatory cannibalism may occur in tadpoles of frogs. But, of the North American species, only the spadefoots as tadpoles show a very marked preference for meat, and only they (some of them) are known to be markedly predaciously cannibalistic.

The earlier workers sometimes noted that the large gray or brown tadpoles of Hammond's Spadefoot are cannibalistic, but it was thought for many years that this was a special peculiarity of this species. Ball (1936) collected tadpoles of Eastern Spadefoot from a large aggregation in a pool in Connecticut and confined them in containers over night. On later examination, he found these confined tadpoles attacking each other viciously and thought that they probably had done so in the pool, although he had not noticed it there. Some years later (Bragg, 1941a) I noted that tadpoles of Hammond's Spadefoot at Las Vegas, New Mexico, differed very markedly in size at the same age in a single pool (Fig. 12), and I speculated that these fast growing larvae might be specialized to feed upon their smaller fellows, but I did not see them do so. Later I found that in Hurter's Spadefoot, as well as in the Plains Spadefoot, tadpoles that had left the water and had tails partly shriveled might, if they re-entered the water, be attacked by others not yet emerged, and that such attacks were upon their shriveling tails. This was, of course, technically speaking cannibalism, but it might not indicate *real* predation, since the attacking tadpoles might be reacting to the fast degenerating tails as to any piece of dead meat. (I have recently seen tad-poles of the Plains Spadefoot attack the legs of those recently metamorphosed, which they had not attacked as tadpoles.)

This is still the only type of cannibalistic predation known in Hurter's Spadefoot in nature (Blair, 1955, noted a small amount in artificially raised tadpoles), but recent developments in the Plains Spadefoot are quite startling and surprisingly different. In order to make this understood it will be necessary to digress from cannibalism long enough to tell another closely related story about the specialization in the feeding mechanism of the Spea group of spadefoots.

During the years of the development of knowledge of our North American frogs and toads, a few workers have centered their interests, partly at least, on the distinctive characters of the larvae. How can one tell the tadpoles of one species from those of another? Dr. A. H. Wright of Cornell University has long been a leading student in this field, but other people have occasionally described tadpoles of certain species heretofore unknown. There are still several undescribed tadpoles and others known imperfectly in our North American species.

The mouth region of a typical tadpole externally is a funnel, fringed partly or wholly by sensory papillae. Inside the funnel, dorsal to and in front of the jaws, are transverse rows of labial denticles commonly called labial teeth. Similarly placed rows of denticles also occur ventrally so that the "lips" (labia) con-stitute efficient scrapers for the gathering of algae or other food materials. Inside the labia at the base of the funnel, there are horny jaws known as upper and lower mandibles; behind these is the mouth cavity itself opening backward into the pharynx.

The arrangement of the rows of labial teeth varies more or less consistently between species or other groups and this is also true of the details as to their position, size and distribution;

and the size, number, and position of papillae also vary as do the size and shape of the jaws. All of these taken together have long been used to help distinguish one type of tadpole from another. Such characters have been found very useful for this purpose, in spite of the minor variations in them noticed within any one species. All such structures are temporary; even the horny jaws are lost during metamorphosis. They are to be considered, therefore, as wholly larval adaptations for feeding during the aquatic phase of each individual's life.

The spadefoots as a group are exceptionally variable in these characters, especially in the number and distribution of the rows of labial teeth, but until recently each type seemed to have a rather distinctive pattern, in spite of this. When I started my work on spadefoots something over 20 years ago, only a few studies had been reported on the characteristics of spadefoot larval mouth parts. Wright (1929) had studied one, thought to be the western form and named accordingly (*Scaphiopus hammondi*). Couch's Spadefoot and the Eastern Spadefoot tadpoles were also known (Wright 1929, 1931), and H. M. Smith (1934) had just described and figured what he took to be the tadpoles of the Plains Spadefoot (*Scaphiopus bombifrons*). Others at that time were unknown, but all have been studied to some extent since then.

Gilmore (1924) in Colorado, soon followed by Storer (1925) in California, found larger and smaller spadefoot tadpoles in the same pools (as I did later in New Mexico), and Gilmore, especially, suspected that the larger ones might be cannibalistic on their fellows. Gilmore's specimens were supposed to be of the Plains Spadefoot (*Scaphiopus bombifrons*) but they did not quite fit with Smith's later idea when he described, under this name, tadpoles from New Mexico with peculiar mouthparts like some but not others of Gilmore's specimens.

At about this time students in Oklahoma entered the picture.

Albert and Minnie Trowbridge, then graduate students at the University of Oklahoma, collected local spadefoots from breeding congresses, sat up all night on several occasions waiting for captured pairs to lay their eggs and then reared these to tadpoles. I had no real part in this but did accompany them on their collecting trips and watched their work. It was Albert Trowbridge who first introduced me to the spadefoots.

The adults used in this way by the Trowbridges, were identified independently as Plains Spadefoots (*Scaphiopus bombifrons*) by several different competent authorities but the tadpoles reared from their eggs compared in all particulars to the western form (*Scaphiopus hammondi*) as Dr. Wright had described it. This seemed to be an impossible situation. Obviously, something was wrong somewhere. Trying to resolve the difficulty, Minnie Trowbridge sent adults and the tadpoles which their eggs had produced to an authority, asking identification of each but not telling him the source of the tadpoles. As expected, he identified the adults as of one species (*bombifrons*) and the tadpoles as of the other (*hammondi*). This was the situation in the spring of 1940.

I was, therefore, keenly aware of this problem when I went for the summer of that year to Las Vegas, New Mexico. Twice during that summer spadefoots bred about Las Vegas and I found that two kinds were there, that known as *bombifrons* in central Oklahoma and another which I identified as *hammondi* but which I had never before seen alive. What kind of tadpoles would each produce? Here was a golden opportunity to find out and I did my best to make the most of it during both breeding periods, one in July and the other in August.

I discovered that only a few pools (of several in which spadefoots bred) had both species in them. Picking out pools in which only one kind could be heard (their voices are quite different) I later watched the development of tadpoles of each type. At the proper time, I then extensively sampled these pools for types of tadpoles present and compared them with the descriptions as given by Drs. Smith and Wright. I found consistently that adults like those in central Oklahoma (*bombifrons*) produced tadpoles like those that the Trowbridges had studied and that the other adults (*hammondi*) produced tadpoles conforming to the description given by Dr. Smith for *bombifrons*. I concluded that, due to earlier difficulties with classification, parents had been confounded and names accordingly applied to the tadpoles in reverse, so to speak. I thought that Dr. Wright had actually described the tadpoles of *bombifrons* under the wrong name and that this had led Dr. Smith astray when he described the other type of tadpole. This seemed to settle the matter satisfactorily to everyone and was widely accepted. In fact, Dr. Smith wrote me a congratulatory note for quickly getting the matter settled.

But again the spadefoots fooled us. The matter was not settled at all! In order to understand why not, it appears necessary to contrast these two types of tadpoles.

The one (then supposedly of *Scaphiopus bombifrons*) has a round body with fully rounded abdomen. The jaws are serrated, but both upper and lower ones make a gentle curve from one side of the mouth to the other, and they fit together in a gently curving line (Fig. 15a). The rows of labial teeth vary considerably in individuals, with the more typical specimens having four rows above and four below when fully developed. The individual labial teeth are usually very dark, prominent, and easily seen with a low powered microscope. The head merges gently with the body so that each well-fed tadpole suggests a lop-sided marble or a subspherical bird's egg with a rather short tail. In some that are very well fed, the abdomen bulges out on each side of the tail, giving the body a shape suggesting a mammalian heart.

The other type of tadpole (supposedly of *Scaphiopus ham-mondi*) grows to a much larger size at the same age, usually has a lean, not-so-rounded abdomen, and its head bulges out to the sides due to the presence of exceptionally large jaw muscles there. The jaws are distinctive. The upper mandible has a very prominent and sharp, serrated beak in the middle with a corresponding deep notch in the lower jaw into which the beak fits as the jaws are closed (Fig. 15b). The labial teeth are small, fine and difficult to see, especially in some rows, and some rows are represented by only a few teeth where one might expect a complete row. The whole appearance is of a tadpole in the process of losing the labial teeth while develop-ing a beak and notched jaws associated with a different method of feeding, and, of course, the prominent jaw muscles which widen and flatten the head suggest the same thing.

Soon after my paper concerned with the New Mexico study was published (Bragg, 1941b) my former associate, Dr. Charles Clinton Smith, collected puzzling spadefoot tadpoles in the pan-handle of Oklahoma. They seemed intermediate between the types as just described. Each looked like a *bombifrons* tad-pole in general but many had weakly developed beaks and notches in the jaws. We did not know quite what to make of them. Several years later, in southwestern Oklahoma, a field assistant collecting tadpoles under my direction brought his apparatus ashore and I immediately spotted a single, large, flat-headed tadpole among the hundreds of *Scaphiopus bombi-frons* and wiggling young salamanders which he had caught. Sure enough, it had the right mouth parts, beak, notch, and everying else to make it a typical *hammondi*. I was elated because no one had known that Hammond's Spadefoot occur-red this far east, although it had been suspected for some time. During the next few years all over western Oklahoma I found the same thing—a pool here and there, with spadefoot tadpoles, mostly of the *bombifrons* type but with a very few of the *hammondi* type admixed. Almost invariably I also found with them many intermediates in various degrees. Then, one day, I really found the explanation for all of this, or so I thought! I came upon a large pool that had so many spadefoot tadpoles in it as to suggest a tadpole soup. But almost all of them were in a very agitated school, each trying to tear others to pieces. The whole water surface scintillated in the sun, disturbed by their efforts as great cloud-like masses of tadpoles plowed through the water. What I was observing was mass predaceous cannibalism. Twenty or thirty tadpoles examined at random gave evidence of all these being *bombifrons,* and I saw none of the large flatheaded type among them. I accordingly reported this as the first known predaceous cannibalism in the Plains Spadefoot (Bragg, 1946).

But the next year at this same place, I found both types present together along with many intermediates, and I then went back to the hundreds collected and preserved the year before. I found that a few in this first group also had intermediate mouth parts, so few that I had not seen any in the sample studied earlier.

Now, it must be remembered that the tadpoles of the western form (*hammondi*) had long been known to be cannibalistic, whereas those of the Plains form (*bombifrons*) were thought not to be so. It, therefore, seemed quite obvious that a few individuals of the western spadefoot (*hammondi*), being present at the extreme eastern limit of their geographic range and stimulated to breed by the same factors to which the Plains form reacted, had entered a breeding congress of the Plains Spadefoot and interbred with them. This seemed all the more likely since it had just then been proved beyond reasonable doubt that some kinds of closely related garden toads (*Bufo*) could interbreed. If they could do so, why could not spadefoots? Indeed, we now are certain that they can do so from the work of Dr. Wasserman earlier cited. Assuming interbreeding, the intermediate tadpoles were explained quite nicely as was also the cannibalistic tendencies seen earlier, these also coming from a known genetic tendency of the western form.

I was so sure of this explanation that I repudiated my own interpretation of the observations of cannibalism in the *bombifrons* tadpoles (Bragg, 1948), now attributing the behavior to the influence of *hammondi* hybrids with perhaps a few true *hammondi* among them. But this was not the explanation, and my misinterpretation of the facts under my nose illustrates again the prime necessity for a critical approach in science and the need always and forever of being confirmed by other workers in the search for truth.

Soon after the events cited took place I received a request from Dr. Robert C. Stebbins to send him some tadpoles to use in descriptions in his forthcoming book.[3] When this appeared, Dr. Stebbins noted that spadefoot tadpoles which I had sent him, declaring them to be *Scaphiopus bombifrons,* varied toward *Scaphiopus hammondi* as we then understood it. Because of this, he questioned whether the characters of the mouth parts (beak, notch, etc.) would really separate the two forms as everyone then thought. The next year Turner (1952) also reported spadefoot tadpoles which had intermediate mouth parts from widely separated regions. He called these Hammond's Spadefoot.

It remained, however, for Dr. Grace L. Orton (1954) to clarify the situation and set all of us on what now seems to be the right track. She reported a single tadpole from a region hundreds of miles east of the Hammond's Spadefoot's range, which had mouth parts exactly as described for that form. She

[3] *Amphibians of Western North America,* University of California Press, 1951.

further noted that the real explanation was to be found in that the Plains Spadefoot must be assumed to have not one, but two kinds of tadpoles, the one predaciously cannibalistic, the other not, and that presumably other species of the Spea group were similar. At least they needed to be examined to find out.

It was not long before I found Miss Orton to be entirely correct so far as *Scaphiopus bombifrons* in Oklahoma is concerned (Bragg, 1957). The species does indeed have two kinds of tadpoles, a most unexpected situation, one with the characters thought earlier to be of *Scaphiopus hammondi* and the other with those thought to be typical of *Scaphiopus bombifrons*.

In my confirmation of this in 1957 I could cite only a single certainly known, predaciously cannibalistic *Scaphiopus bombifrons* tadpole from a single pool. I WATCHED this larva eat eight others, approximately one each day. Since then, my son (who joined me in this study) and I have seen several others in natural waters attack, kill and eat their fellows, and there now seems to be no question about it (Bragg and Bragg, 1958).

But where does this leave us concerning the tadpole of Hammond's spadefoot? Was I mistaken also in my studies at Las Vegas? Did I confuse cannibalistic tadpoles of *Scaphiopus bombifrons* with those of *Scaphiopus hammondi?* I still do not think so because I am certain about the adults being of two kinds and I am quite certain about their segregation into different pools during the breeding congresses seen. Assuming that I am right in these things, then there is, as of now, no characteristic known by which one can be certain to which of the two species a tadpole belongs if he does not know the locality from which it came to be occupied by one but not by the other species. As Miss Orton strongly emphasized, there are still many things to be learned about tadpoles of the whole spadefoot group, especially in Spea.

JUVENILE BEHAVIOR

The larval period ends, of course, with the transformation to the adult form as already detailed. But in no sense can we call the animals adults at this time. Depending upon its species and upon its "luck" in getting food during the tadpole stage, a spadefoot is anywhere from the size of a housefly to that of the outer section of a man's thumb when it is first fully transformed. Being quite small, its greatest danger is desiccation, not only because it typically leaves the pool during quite warm or hot weather, but also because the ratio of its surface to its volume is very large. Its radical and very fast change of environment is accordingly accompanied with a wholly new set of behavior patterns associated with its equally radical change in body form. Metamorphosis is so radical a change that it is the most dangerous period physiologically in a spadefoot's life. From a tadpole whose greatest activity is during daylight hours, it quite suddenly becomes a gnome of the night—a seeker of objects under which to hide as a protection from heat—and it now tends to leave such areas only during darkness. Details vary, however, with conditions. If there has been considerable rain, some young spadefoots hop about, day and night, seeking food. If they happen to emerge from a pool during hot, dry weather, they seek protection immediately and leave it only at night.

Species also differ. Young juveniles of the Plains Spadefoot, emerging in hot weather, quite commonly start burrowing immediately into the soil (usually the softer, moist area about their natal pool). Sometimes they do this before the tail has been fully absorbed. Hurter's Spadefoot at this stage has never been known to do so. These always seek objects under which to hide. Apparently they do not know how to burrow at this stage, although it takes them only a few days for their instinctive pattern of burrowing to be perfected. Once, several years ago, I watched the transformation of thousands of Hurter's Spadefoots from an exposed pool during very hot weather. There were only a few suitable objects for their protection about the pool (a few leaves, one mass of dried cow dung, and a small piece of wood). The sun shone very brightly, there was a strong south wind, and the air temperature was 109° F. Evaporation rate was so high that one could almost see the water go! But not one of these tiny toads tried to burrow. Every available object was used to its capacity, however, and all the space under each was completely filled with little toads two or three layers deep. But there was not enough space for all, and hundreds died on the pool's edge because they lost water more rapidly through their exposed skins than they could absorb it through their bellies. I was interested to note that none of them went back into the pool (as any little frog would have done) although many were only a few inches from it when they succumbed. A Plains Spadefoot, under these circumstances, would have backed into the mud and lived.

On the other hand, if the conditions of temperature are not too severe and, especially if the whole ground is moist, young juveniles of Hurter's Spadefoot may be out feeding during the daytime. Quite commonly they scatter widely before their first morning out of the water. Within a day or two, they probably begin burrows for themselves, although this has not been observed in nature. I have had captives of this age burrow in soil provided them, however, and I have usually failed to find any of the thousands emerging from a pool within a few days, except when the ground is quite moist. In general, the little juveniles of spadefoots seem in a hurry to get away from the natal pool as soon as conditions permit. Sometimes there is a mass migration, almost social in character. This has never been seen in any species of Spea nor in Hurter's or Couch's Spade-foots, but it is not unexpected. Neill (1957) gives an interesting account of it as seen in the Eastern Spadefoot. He came upon thousands of young juveniles all progressing in the same direc-tion. Since the adults of this form eventually occupy home burrows, spaced about right so that each has a feeding terri-tory sufficient for its needs (Pearson, 1955), it seems probable that such a migrating group eventually breaks down as each little toad finds an unoccupied territory in which to construct its home burrow. But nobody, so far as I know, has seen this done.

As noted earlier, the juveniles feed ravenously on small arthropods, gradually adapting to larger prey as they them-selves increase in size. A group emerging in May may reach one third to one half adult size by fall, if one can judge by the captive animals which I have studied. It is unknown for any species at what size or age they become reproductive and thus fully adult. I do have a few observations bearing on this point, but they are quite inadequate to prove anything. Here they are for what they are worth.

A single captive tadpole of the Plains Spadefoot metamor-phosed in May and was put into a box of earth over which a light burned each night to attract insects. The little toad grew rapidly and was about one third adult size in August when it often failed to emerge on nights for feeding. In September I transferred it to another container of earth in a warm room where it burrowed into the soil and stayed there. In February, I dug it out to be used to make a tape recording of the juvenile protesting note of its species, which differs from that of an adult. When stimulated, however, it gave the protesting note of an adult male and seemed to have the secondary sex characters of that sex well developed. Had I caught this little fellow in nature and not known its age, I would have thought it without question to be a small adult. This suggests that this individual had become sexually mature in about nine months.

This would seem quite adequate except for the following : I have had other juveniles of this species, kept in the same way. On February 13, 1958, I dug one out which was still unquestionably not an adult, although only slightly smaller than the first mentioned. Perhaps individuals vary in their rate of progress toward maturity with their success in getting food during their first summer. No one knows yet.

With Hurter's Spadefoot, I have seen many breeding congresses and watched or captured very many males while they were calling, often from pools known to have produced thousands of young the previous year. Yet all that I have ever seen in such a pool were rather large males, never a single one that I would expect from the size of autumn or spring juveniles to be less than two years old.

Since the Plains Spadefoot has small adults and large tadpoles and Hurter's Spadefoot large adults and quite small tadpoles, Hurter's Spadefoot has farther to go in terms of growth than the Plains Spadefoot to reach breeding size. It would therefore seem a reasonable deduction that the Plains Spadefoot might well take a shorter time to reach adulthood. But no one has yet followed this through by observations, and until this is done adequately we cannot be sure. As already shown, even the most seemingly reasonable deductions about spadefoots can be wrong, as in the case of the dimorphic tadpoles in the Spea group.

I have recently made one minor observation on the sexual behavior of juveniles of the Plains Spadefoot. The container occupied by 35 or 40 of these which were still quite small and immature became flooded during a rain. A short time later

I found these animals attempting to clasp each other as they floated on the water. They were very active, swimming about in mated pairs much like the adults, with some of them squeaking their high pitched protesting notes when clasped. This behavior must have been a sort of sexual play resulting from the stimulus of flooding which had called forth the clasping instinct as in adults.

V

Evolution, Habits, and Habitat

LET US NOW SUMMARIZE BRIEFLY SOME OF THE THINGS THAT
we have said about the spadefoot toads to see what type of
general picture emerges if we do not befog it by minor differences in details.

First, we note that this is a very small group of animals as
such groups go, for there are no more than eight present-day
forms and probably only seven. Second, we note that they are
a completely North American group, the great majority
limited to the United States and adjacent northern Mexico.
Third, it is obvious to those who have seen live members of
a toad family known as the Pelobatidae from Asia and
especially Europe that the spadefoots are very closely like these
in many of their physical characteristics. In fact, the majority
of American students now think that *Scaphiopus* is a genus
of this family. Fourth, within the spadefoot group, even
though it *is* small, two groups of forms are clearly recognized,
each sufficiently different to cause some to contend that they
should be subgenera (*Scaphiopus* and *Spea*), others that they
represent two separate genera. Anyone who has examined a
live specimen (as I have) of the European *Pelobates fuscus*

Fig. 1. Couch's Spadefoot *(Scaphiopus couchi* Baird*)* just after being removed from its burrow. Note the large round pupil of the eye which spadefoots show when in the dark. Compare with Fig. 2. (Photo by Mr. Marlin Dobry.)

Fig. 2. The same individual as shown in Fig. 1 after some minutes in bright light. The pupil of the eye is a vertical slit, a characteristic shown among the North American frogs and toads only by spadefoots. Particles of various kinds have been caught by the slime of the skin. (Photo by Mr. Marlin Dobry.)

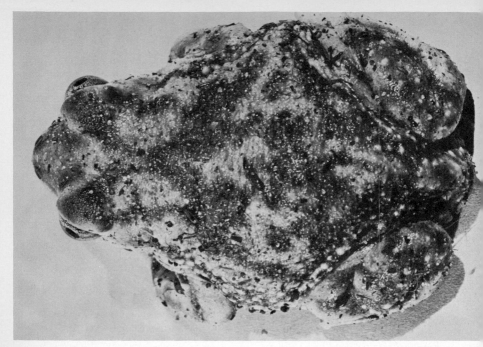

Fig. 3.   Couch's Spadefoot from southwestern Oklahoma showing the characteristic mottling on the back. Some specimens do not show this. (Photo by Mr. Marlin Dobry.)

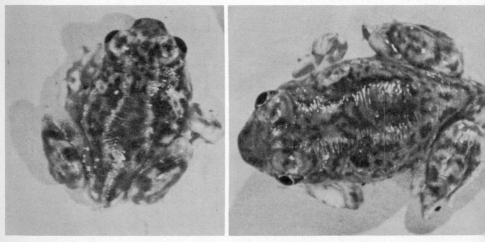

Fig. 4.   An adult (right) and a halfgrown juvenile of the Plains Spadefoot *(Scaphiopus bombifrons* Cope) from central Oklahoma. Note the raised portion between the eyes (the boss) by which this species may be distinguished. *Scaphiopus hammondi hammondi* looks almost exactly like this except that it lacks the boss. *Scaphiopus hammondi intermontanus* has a glandular area here which is soft instead of hard but looks almost exactly like this picture. (Photo by Dr. Charles Clinton Smith.)

Fig. 5. The upper pool mentioned in the text, a characteristic breeding site of Hurter's Spadefoot *(Scaphiopus holbrooki hurteri* Strecker). A single female had laid eggs here the night before this picture was taken in May, as shown in Fig. 6. (Photo by Mr. Marlin Dobry.)

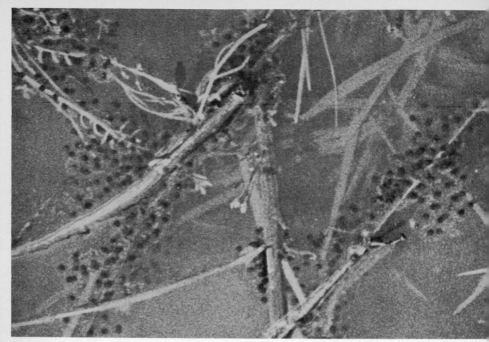

Fig. 6. Portion of a clutch of eggs, photographed through the shallow water as they were left by a pair of spadefoots in the pool shown in Fig. 5. A single large female of Hurter's Spadefoot was seen approaching this pool during a rain the previous evening. These eggs hatched the day after the picture was taken, but the tadpoles were all killed as the pool dried up a few days later. (Photo by Mr. Marlin Dobry.)

Fig. 7. Tadpoles of Hurter's Spadefoot, collected by Dr. Charles C. Smith (accompanied by the author) in Arkansas near the eastern limit of this subspecies' range. They were photographed swimming and feeding in an aquarium a few days later. (Photo by Mr. Marlin Dobry.)

Fig. 8. A tadpole of Hurter's Spadefoot feeding on particles in an aquarium. The light spots are food supplied. (Photo by Mr. Marlin Dobry.)

Fig. 9. Pool in the eastern edge of Las Vegas, New Mexico in which stalked eggs of *Scaphiopus bombifrons* were found in August, 1940. This also illustrates one of the shallowest pools in which this species has been known to breed. (Photo by the author.)

Fig. 10. A temporary pool near Las Vegas, New Mexico. After a violent rain formed the pool in July, 1940, only Hammond's Spadefoot used it for breeding. But after another rain in August, only the Plains Spadefoot used it. This illustrates that these two species do not differentiately select breeding sites but, rather, that the breeding call of the first males reaching a pool tends to determine which species will use a given pool at a given time. Thus the male's breeding call is shown to be one isolating mechanism tending to avoid interbreeding. (Photo by the author.)

Fig. 11. A typical breeding site of the Plains Spadefoot *(Scaphiopus bombifrons)* near Las Vegas, New Mexico. Contrast with the exceptional breeding site shown in Fig. 9. (Photo by the author.)

Fig. 12. Pool containing tadpoles of *Scaphiopus hammondi,* suspected, when the picture was taken, of being cannibalistic. (Photo by the author.)

Fig. 13. A typical breeding site of Hammond's Spadefoot. (Photo by the author.)

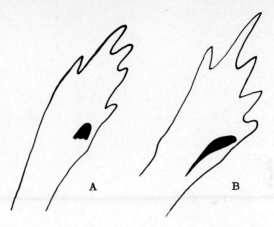

Fig. 14. The hind foot of two spadefoots to show the difference in the spade in the two species groups, Spea and Scaphiopus *(seusu stricto)*. A. *Scaphiopus (Spea) bombifrons* Cope. B. *Scaphiopus (Scaphiopus) holbrooki hurteri* Strecker. In all Spea (A) the spade is at least as wide as long; in all Scaphiopus (B) it is considerably longer than wide. (Drawings from life by Mr. Marlin Dobry.)

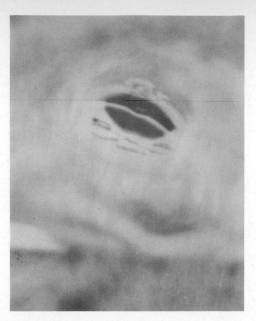

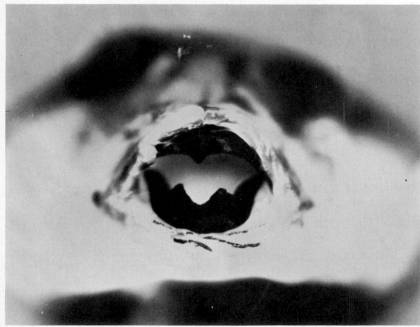

Fig. 15. Looking directly into the opened mouth of two tadpoles of *Scaphiopus bombifrons* to show variations. A. The non-cannibalistic type; B. A known predaceous cannibal. Note particularly the difference in jaws (see text). Details of arrangement of the labial teeth rows vary in both but are usually more irregular in the cannibalistic than in the non-cannibalistic. (Photo furnished by the late Otis M. King.)

Fig. 16. Masses of Hurter's Spadefoot tadpoles on moist mud as all standing water seeped from a pool on a hill top. (Photo by the author.)

Fig. 17. Masses of dead tadpoles of the Plains Spadefoot on the thoroughly dried and cracked bottom of a terrace ditch. Many tadpoles lose the race with evaporation as did these. (Photo by the author.)

Fig. 18. Pool in oak-shinnery in western Oklahoma which contained tadpoles of the Plains Spadefoot when picture was taken. (Photo by the author.)

Fig. 19. Breeding site of Couch's Spadefoot in southwestern Oklahoma. Feeding schools of their tadpoles were found here. (Photo by the author.)

Fig. 20. Aggregated tadpoles of the Plain's Spadefoot at shore line. Individuals were emerging from this mass gradually, whereas others continue to feed. (Photo by the late Otis M. King with the author, June 17, 1959.)

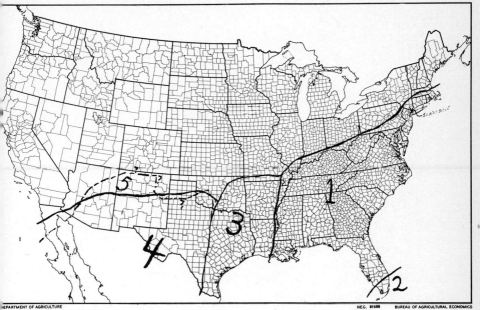

Map. 1. Approximate geographic (not ecological) distribution of spadefoots of subgenus Scaphiopus. 1. *Scaphiopus holbrooki holbrooki* (the Eastern Spadefoot). 2. *S. h. albus* (the Key West Spadefoot) 3. *S. h. hurteri* (Hurter's spadefoot) 4. *S. couchi* (Couch's spadefoot). 5. Areas in which Couch's Spadefoot may occur—its northern limits of distribution are obscure. It may be much farther north than shown.

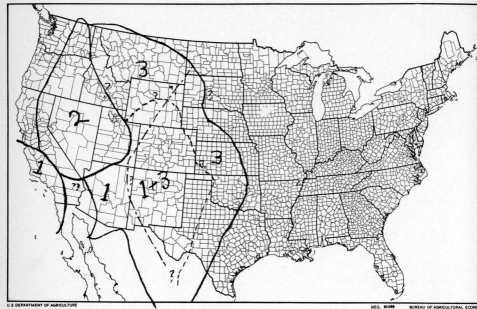

Map. 2. Approximate geographic (not ecological) distribution of spadefoots of the subgenus Spea in U.S.A., Canada, and Northern
Mexico. 1. *Scaphiopus h. hammondi* (Hammond's Spadefoot).
2. *S. h. intermontanus* (the intermountain spadefoot). 3. *S.
bombifrons* (the Plains Spadefoot). 1+3 (between the non-solid
lines)=approximate regions where Hammond's and the Plains
Spadefoot overlap in distribution. Dashed line=approximate
eastern limits of distribution of Hammond's Spadefoot. Dot-
dash line=approximate western limits of distribution of the
Plains Spadefoot. ?= uncertainties. In the Dakotas, especially,
the Plains Spadefoot may occur farther to the east. The
Mexican Spadefoot's distribution is omitted.

fuscus, and compared it with the American spadefoots will have difficulty in showing it to be more different from any member of Scaphiopus (genus) than Scaphiopus (subgenus) differs from Spea. From such considerations it seems clear that the spadefoots are pelobatids which have evolved in two basic directions in morphological characters on the North American continent and that the results of this process are shown in the modern fauna by the two groups (whether called subgenera or genera) obviously present.

The early beginnings of the spadefoots in North America are quite obscure so that we do not know their starting point. A few fossils have been discovered and given names, and we know from the age of the deposits in which some of them have been found that spadefoot-like animals existed before horses, camels, and elephants roamed the North American grasslands in the Pleistocene period. Spadefoots have existed for many thousands of years, but that is about all that geology teaches us concerning them. If, therefore, we wish to find out how they have changed in their evolution, we are forced to look at their structures, distributions and habits to see what reasonable deductions can be made. This has been of use (Zweifel, 1956; Bragg, 1961a). But it should never be overlooked that any ideas obtained by this process (no matter who has them, or how reasonable they sound) *are* deductions, and, as such, are subject to modification or even to discarding entirely if later new pertinent facts come to light which do not fit. Someone has said that many beautiful theories have been wrecked on the hard rocks of facts. The point that I am making is that they should be whenever new facts warrant it.

With this understood, we are now free to do the best we can in speculative and factual deductions about possible evolutionary pathways in the spadefoots. The main point to be made concerns the peculiar specialization in habits.

As noted earlier, all spadefoots show the xeric pattern of breeding behavior characterized by (1) a very loud voice of the male, attractive to members of both sexes; (2) breeding in temporary water, typically in pools just formed by rains; (3) having breeding periods staggered through the warmer months so that not all females "report" for egg laying at any one rainy period, i.e., the spadefoots have no clearcut breeding season in the usual sense.

Now the most striking thing about this type of breeding pattern is that it is shared in its major features by several frogs and toads of North America not at all closely related to spadefoots. Not only in this, but also in many closely related forms in several genera, some species have this pattern whereas others do not. Some species of garden toads *(Bufo)* have it, others have the more typical mesic pattern, and at least one the intermediate pattern. One of the most common narrowmouth frogs *(Microhyla)* of North America has a breeding season, whereas the other follows the rains despite the fact that these two are so much alike in structure as to make it uncertain whether they are both species or only subspecies of one form. In some of the smaller members of the treefrog family (e.g. the genus *Pseudacris*) we find the same thing. What this amounts to is that in their evolution of breeding habits, the North American frogs and toads have developed differently in behavior than they have in structure. Since their classification is based almost entirely on structure, it is impossible to deduce from the breeding pattern of one species what the pattern in a close relative will be. Some features of breeding habits and habit-patterns of this or that species in any of several groups have evolved differently in closely related forms, in all cases closely associated with different adaptive niches in the environment.

Searching for a possible explanation for this state of affairs some years ago, I noted (Bragg, 1944–45, 1950c) that I could find no species of amphibia whose distribution was limited to the grassland and desert areas in North America which did not show the main features of the xeric pattern of breeding behavior. Accordingly, I thought that some feature or features in the grassland environment (including the deserts and semi-deserts of the Southwest) must be responsible. This seems to follow, since "nature is interested in survival of the race" not of the individual as such, and the weakest point in life cycles usually involves the development of the young which, alone, continue the species. This seemed to be a clear case of survival of the fittest, as Herbert Spencer long ago called this Dar-winian factor in evolution. The "fittest" frog and toad-like amphibians in the North American grasslands and deserts are clearly those which show what I have called the xeric pattern of breeding. And this pattern is even shown by the one kind of salamander able to live in the Plains.

I also noted that most species along the eastern border of the United States do not have this pattern. They, instead, typically have a more or less clear-cut breeding season. The biggest exception is the Eastern Spadefoot. Why should this be?

Dr. Tanner's suggestion in 1939 that the spadefoots arose as a group in the Sonoran region and spread out from there seems a good solution, for, as explained earlier, the xeric pat-tern is a prime necessity in dry areas. It enables a population to use the water for breeding purposes whenever it happens to be available. This in some places is not very often. Pre-sumably, therefore, the ancestral spadefoots, as a part of their adaptation to dry areas, were subjected to exceptionally severe selection in favor of those which varied toward the xeric pattern, until only those having it in marked degree survived.

These eventually became Scaphiopus, probably early in the present era.

But spadefoots are like other organisms in that each attempts to occupy as much of the earth as possible so that they spread over the continent, changing into the types now known (and others now extinct).

It is probably true that the first basic changes resulted in the two species-groups now recognized, i.e., Spea and Scaphiopus *(sensu stricto)*. In each group the larvae were also subjected to high selection pressure in the fast disappearing, temporary pools where the eggs are typically laid. Inherently fast development and special abilities to secure the often limited food supply were at a premium, and hence the tadpoles developed most or all of their peculiarities of behavior mentioned earlier.

Whereas the Spea group remained in the West for the most part, all but one of the other found niches to the east. Couch's Spadefoot remained in the grasslands and developed with (and, in habits, more like) Spea. Hurter's Spadefoot now forms a link in distribution between the western and the eastern forms, whereas the Eastern Spadefoot has spread its distribution widely over the East, merging along its western border in eastern Arkansas, for example, with Hurter's form.

Turning again to habits, it is to be emphasized that a species with the xeric pattern of breeding is not at a reproductive disadvantage in a region with plenty of rainfall. Hence, the Eastern Spadefoot, with its firmly fixed xeric pattern, lives well in the more mesic East. This species, therefore, has not changed materially the ways of doing things that its ancestor "found good" in the grasslands or desert and which the western species still find necessary. This explanation has recently been emphasized also by Hansen (1958). Even the cannibalism which spadefoot tadpoles sometimes manifest is biologically sound, for most of the thousands of little spade-foots produced from a successful breeding period have little chance of surviving. If every spadefoot egg laid should result in an adult spadefoot there would soon be no room on the face of the earth for anything else.

This being the case among all spadefoots, if the limited food supply of a desert pool can, through cannibalistic activities, be concentrated into the growth and development of a few soon enough for these to emerge from the water ahead of its evaporation, then the species is saved by the survival of a few hundred young, some of which have a chance to grow to reproductive size and age and thus continue the life of the species. Without some method of securing sufficient food, all tadpoles in a given pool are in danger of developing too slowly so that none are ready to emerge as the water goes. If all are killed, none serve the species. Indeed, if anything they hinder it through wasting the food concentrated in the eggs from which they came, so laborously collected and con-centrated by the mother spadefoot. On the other hand, at least in Hurter's Spadefoot, even those tadpoles which fail in a given pool may still unconsciously help their kind by serving not only as food but also as an accelerating factor in metamor-phosis when eaten by oncoming generations, as I have demon-strated several times.

Very recently (Bragg, 1962, 1964a) several new observations on spadefoot tadpoles have been made which bear upon some of the problems outlined. In the spring of 1961 a pool con-tained tadpoles of two species *(Scaphiopus bombifrons* and *Scaphiopus couchi)* of the same size and age (eight days after the only rain there which could have stimulated breeding of the adults). Some of the *Scaphiopus bombifrons* were attacking and eating the *Scaphiopus couchi* tadpoles. However, in the laboratory it was found that none of these were of the cannibalistic type. In a few days these predatory tadpoles (and only these) became real giants of the species and were the first to metamorphose. As the pool shrank rapidly the *Scaphiopus couchi* formed metamorphic aggregations from which they emerged successfully. Only about half of the *Scaphiopus bombifrons* emerged in time, however. Yet the other half of them did so, which clearly indicated two groups with different developmental rates in the same water. It was strongly suspected that those which succeeded had had their developmental rate increased by their predatory activities, but this was not proved.

Accordingly, in the spring of 1962 this place was revisited at the proper time. Again, both species had bred here a few days before. But this time, cannibalistic type *Scaphiopus bombifrons* occurred. Laboratory study showed that (1) all of these were predatory on any smaller spadefoot tadpoles; (2) some (but not all) non-cannibalistic *Scaphiopus bombifrons* were predatory on *Scaphiopus couchi;* (3) *Scaphiopus couchi* were not predatory on other tadpoles but would eat dead ones of any kind present; (4) *Scaphiopus couchi* tadpoles had a much faster developmental rate than *Scaphiopus bombifrons* provided that the latter had not eaten other tadpoles. Those of the latter which did so, whether of their own kind or not, became giant tadpoles, and some of them metamorphosed at about the same time as most of the *Scaphiopus couchi.*

This seemed to mean that eating other tadpoles of whatever kind enormously increases the growth rate and speeds the developmental rate as well. Thus, we see another proof of the adaptive significance of predation and cannibalism on the spadefoot tadpoles of *Spea.*

In addition, the intrinsically faster rate of development in *Scaphiopus couchi* saves many lives through merely getting them out of the water ahead of some of the predatory

Scaphiopus bombifrons In the same way, the predatory *Scaphiopus bombifrons* (whether cannabalistic or not) by emerging early, leave the way free for their slower fellows to emerge later if further rains refill the pool or if all the water does not evaporate too soon.

What this all amounts to is a small group of species, primarily and nicely adapted, both as adults and tadpoles, to life in very dry regions. Having met successfully the very dangerous period of reproduction and larval development through severe selection pressure, every spadefoot now has the pattern of behavior described firmly fixed in its heredity. Some species, like the eastern form, have moved into regions where such patterns of behavior are, on the average, no longer necessary. But since these patterns in the new environment do little or no harm, the animals have not been subjected to other severe selection pressures tending to change them. Hence they have retained in their present environment their basic behavior patterns which originally adapted them to desert life.

This does not imply that some small changes have not been made, of course. Every species (and even subspecies) differs at least slightly in habits from all others. What I mean to indicate is that they have not changed the basic features of the habit patterns. Some species which remained in the dry regions not only retained all of the basic habit patterns but have begun new specializations among the tadpoles. This is probably the real meaning of the dimorphism with predaceous cannibalism recently recognized in Spea.

It has taken over a century of observations and deductions, theorizing, criticizing, and the modifying of ideas, involving many naturalists to see this picture clearly. Partly, this was because of the fact that the first spadefoots were studied in the mesic regions of the East. As early as 1884 Charles C. Abbott in New Jersey noted cannibalism and aggregational feeding in the Eastern Spadefoot tadpoles, and he correctly deduced that this might have something to do with their lives in temporary pools. But he was completely mystified by the exceptionally loud voices of the calling males. He wrote :

"I have already referred to the wonderful noises made by these animals when they congregate in pools for the purpose of spawning. At no other time do they appear to be vocal, and the question naturally arises, why, when the animals lead a life that requires no such power except for two or three days in a year, should its utterances be far louder than any or all the frogs and toads of the same locality combined? Although the animal is strictly crepuscular and not diurnal, it could readily find a mate guided by sight and the purpose of the deafening epithalamium is somewhat hard to determine. If it could be shown that they call to each other from far distant points, the difficulty would disappear, but this they are not known to do. Apparently, it is not until they are congregated in some available pool that they sing, if singing it can be called. No words yet in use in our language can fairly describe their utterances, which, it may be presumed, are expressions of delight at meeting."

Actually, of course, what the spadefoot male is shouting so loudly is, in essence, "Come quickly for I have found a good pool for breeding," and he *is* actually calling to others which may be a mile away, although no one now thinks that he is self-conscious about it. He calls because it is fundamental in his nature to call in such circumstances, and his voice is loud and carries far because, although unknown to him, it serves his species to get the reproductive process started as quickly as possible.

Similarly, the burrowing habits of the Eastern Spadefoot and the fact that years might pass in a given place with none being seen puzzled the earlier naturalists, especially since the spadefoots might suddenly appear in large numbers and call lustily after a heavy rain as Dr. Abbott so graphically noted. Gradually the idea grew that this spadefoot must spend months or years at a time underground, emerging only exceptionally to breed and then going back into the ground where they seemed to "pull the hole in after them."

As biology in the East gradually went into the experimental phase in about 1895, fewer and fewer observations were made in the out-of-doors where the animals live. But in the less developed West, where ecological studies and biological surveys were still developing, the habits of the spadefoots in their more characteristic homeground gradually showed the true condition. The Eastern Spadefoot seemed peculiar and exceptional in its way of doing things because it is an animal basically adapted to a xeric environment but living in a mesic habitat now. While well adjusted in minor details at present to life in the more moist East, it carried its basic behavior patterns with it as it differentiated from desert ancestors. (See Bragg, 1961, for a fuller discussion.)

I know almost nothing first hand about other pelobatids. Several species in other genera in China are adapted quite differently. The tadpoles live in rapids and small side pools in streams. Some of them look like frog tadpoles, and others have funnel-shaped mouths or expanded lips associated with surface feeding. The breeding period (season?) of the adults extends over several months. These observations came from Pope[4] and the authors cited by him. Such animals would seem to be quite different in their adaptive habits from the spadefoots.

[4] Pope, Clifford H. Notes on Amphibians from Fukien, Hainan, and other parts of China. Bulletin of the American Museum of Natural History, 61 Article, 8: 397–611, 1931.

Pelobates fuscus, with several subspecies in Eurasia, how-ever, does show some similarities. It is sometimes called the European Spadefoot. According to Savage[5], *Pelobates fuscus fuscus* burrows much like the American *Scaphiopus.* It some-times fails to emerge in the evening, but when it does so it follows the local time wherever it happens to be. He could find little which might act as a stimulus to emergence, and he wondered how the toad "could tell the time" underground. I have often wondered about this, too, for *Scaphiopus.* Appeal-ing to animal rhythms or biological clocks, as often done, *explains* nothing; it merely gives such phenomena a name.

Tadpoles of *Pelobates* as compared to those of *Scaphiopus* are intermediate in size, smaller than those of the Spea group, larger than those of the other if I may judge from two lots of known age kindly sent me from near Rostock, East Germany, by Dr. M. Meyer, and their eyes are placed quite differently.[6] But their behavior may have some features in common with their American cousins. In correspondence Mr. Ion E. Fuhn of Bucarest, Romania, remarked (my translation from his letter to me in French), "Two species of *Pelobates* live in Romania, *Pelobates fuscus fuscus* and *Pelobates syriacus balkanicus,* Karaman. I have also seen gregarious behavior *(comfortement gregaire)* in our *Pelobates fuscus* as well as in tadpoles of *Bufo bufo.* The conditions of the medium were in favor of a nutritional explanation." I know nothing more than this about the European Spadefoots, but Mr. Fuhn's observation may well indicate that on the European steppes *Pelobates* has had

[5] Savage, R. Maxwell. On the Burrowing and Emergence of the Spade-foot Toad. Proceedings of the Zoological Society of London, 112 (Section A): 21–35, 1942.

[6] Giant tadpoles sometimes occur. One is recorded from Sweden measuring 105 mm. by Gislen and Kauri (*Acta Vertabratica* 1 (3): 207, 1959). Recall that *Scaphiopus* tadpoles also sometimes reach exception-ally large size both in Scaphiopus and Spea, more commonly in the former, especially predatory ones.

an evolution in habit patterns in some ways comparable to the North American *Scaphiopus*. It would be well for naturalists of eastern Europe and adjacent Asia to find out.

One wonders also what the situation is in and along the edges of the Sahara in Africa, in the Arabian countries such as Iraq, in Iran, and in adjacent regions near the Red Sea, in and near the Gobi desert of Asia and in the interior of Australia. Wherever desert conditions are caused by dryness rather than by cold (as in the desert of Atacama in South America) it may well be that some species of frogs, toads, or their relatives have developed specializations in habits similar to those of the spadefoots here described or have developed other ways of accomplishing continuing life in such regions. Until interested naturalists living in such regions can make observations in nature, we do not know, of course. In the meantime, further intensive studies on our own spadefoots to elucidate further the many unanswered questions already noted may be expected to broaden and deepen our understanding of the behavior of xerically adapted amphibians. There is still much to do, and few yet to do it.

Appendix

The following key is based upon contrasting groups of characters. To determine the species in hand read the lines marked 1 and 1' and look at the specimen to determine which statement comes closer to describing its characters. Each statement (after 1) is followed by another number (as 2 or 4) or a name. Go to this number and repeat the process till a name is substituted for a number. This is the name of the species or subspecies in hand.

1. Pupil of the eye after some time in bright light not a *vertical* slit .... not a spadefoot.

1' Pupil in bright light a vertical slit (Fig. 2) ....
Spadefoot Toads 2

2. Spade elongate, narrow, at least twice as long as wide, sickle shaped (Fig. 14B). Color usually dark (green to nearly black, usually with light dorsal markings, sometimes mottled) .... (subgenus Scaphiopus) 3

2' Spade short, rounded, nearly as wide as long, not sickle shaped (Fig. 14A). Color usually light (brown or gray) ...
(subgenus Spea) 5

3. Back with two elongate light areas nearer together near midback, suggesting an hour-glass in shape 4

3' Back without light hour-glass shaped areas. Color uniform on back (grey or green to black) or with a few large irregular spots with mottling on the ground color (Fig. 3)
Couch's Spadefoot *(Scaphiopus couchi)*

109

4. With a distinct raised portion (boss) behind the eyes, the skin of which bears many fine dark spines.....................
Hurter's Spadefoot *(Scaphiopus holbrooki hurteri)* (Frontispiece).

4' With little or no boss behind eyes and without (or with very few) spines ....
Eastern Spadefoot *(Scaphiopus holbrooki holbrooki)*

5. Skin smooth, with no or very few suggestions of tubercles : often with a few irregular red spots on back and sometimes with lighter markings as well 6

5' Skin warty with various sized tubercles ....
Mexican Spadefoot *(Scaphiopus multiplicatus)*

6. A distinct *bony* boss just in front of the eyes, in large individuals making a depression between the eyes and nostrils (Fig. 4) .... Plains Spadefoot *(Scaphiopus bombifrons)*

6' No bony boss present (soft glandular mass may take its place). 7

7. A soft glandular mass just anterior to the eyes giving the animal the general appearance of having a boss ....
Great Basin Spadefoot *(Scaphiopus hammondi intermontanus)*

7' No glandular mass before eyes ....
Hammond's Spadefoot *(Scaphiopus hammondi hammondi)*

Selected References

Major articles, or those thought to contain observations of special interest are marked with an asterisk.

Abbott, C. C.
  1884. Recent studies of the spadefoot toad. American Naturalist, 18 : 1075–1080.

Allen, M. F.
  1932. Further comments of the activity of the spade-foot toad. Copeia 1932(2) : 104.

Axtell, R. W., and Aaron O. Wassermen.
  1953. Interesting herpetological records from southern Texas and northern Mexico. Herpetologica, 9 : 1–6.

Babbitt, L. H.
  1932. Some remarks on Connecticut herpetology. Bulletin of the Boston Society Natural History, 63 : 25.

*Ball, Stanley C.
  1936. The distribution and behavior of the spadefoot toad in Connecticut. Transactions of the Connecticut Academy of Arts and Science, 32 : 351–379.

Blair, A. P.
  1947. Field observations on spadefoot toads. Copeia 1947(1). 67.

Blair, A. P., C. C. Hargreaves, and K. K. Chen.
  1940. Susceptibility of spadefoot toad and tree frog to ouabain, cymarin, and conmingine hydrochloride. Proceedings of the Society of Experimental Biology and Medicine, 45 : 209–214.

Blair, W. F.

1949. Development of the solitary spadefoot in Texas. Copeia 1949(1) : 72.

1955. Differentiation of mating call in spadefoots, genus Scaphiopus. Texas Journal of Science, 7(2) : 183–188.

1956. Mating call and possible stage of speciation of the Great Basin spadefoot. Texas Journal of Science, 8 : 236–238.

Bragg, Arthur N.

1940. Observations on the ecology and natural history of Anura. III. The ecological distribution of Anura in Cleveland County, Oklahoma, with notes on the habits of several species. American Midland Naturalist, 24 : 322–335.

Bragg, Arthur N.

1941. Observations on the ecology and natural history of Anura. VIII. Some factors in the initiation of breeding behavior. Turtox News, 19 : 10–12.

1941a. Some observations on Amphibia at and near Las Vegas, New Mexico. The Great Basin Naturalist, 2 : 109–117.

1941b. Tadpoles of *Scaphiopus bombifrons* and *Scaphiopus hammondii*. The Wasmann Collector, 4 : 92–94.

1942. Key to spadefoot toads (Scaphiopus) in Oklahoma. Turtox News, 20 : 154.

1942a. On toad and frog abundance after heavy rainfall. Science, 95 : 194–195.

1942b. Further field notes on the initiation of breeding behavior of Anura. Turtox News, 20 : 12–13.

* 1944. Observations on the ecology and natural history of Anura. XIII. Breeding habits, eggs and tadpoles of *Scaphiopus hurterii*. Copeia 1944(4) 230–240.

* 1944–45. Observations on the ecology and natural history of Anura. XII. The spadefoot toads in Oklahoma with a summary of our knowledge of the group. American Naturalist, 78 : 517–533 and 79 : 52–72.

1945. Notes on the psychology of frogs and toads. Journal General Psychology, 32 : 27–37.

1945a. Aggregational phenomena in *Scaphiopus hurterii* tadpoles. Proceedings of the Oklahoma Academy of Science, 26 : 19.

* 1945b. Breeding and tadpoles behavior in *Scaphiopus hurterii* near Norman, Oklahoma, spring, 1945. The Wasmann Collector, 6 : 69–78.

* 1946. Aggregation with cannibalism in tadpoles of *Scaphiopus bombifrons* with some general remarks on the probable evolutionary significance of such phenomena. Herpetologica, 3 : 89–96.

1946a. Aggregations in tadpoles of spadefoot toads (abst.). Anatomical Record, 94 : 351–352.

*Bragg, Arthur N.

1946b. Some salientian adaptations. The Great Basin Naturalist, 7 : 1–4.

1947. Tadpole behavior in pools and streams. Proceedings of the Oklahoma Academy of Science, 27 : 59–61.

1948. Additional instances of social aggregations in tadpoles. The Wasmann Collector, 7 : 66–79.

1950. Identification of Salientia in Oklahoma. Researches on the Amphibia of Oklahoma. Art. 1 : 9–29. University of Oklahoma Press, Norman, Oklahoma.

1950a. Salientian breeding dates in Oklahoma. Researches on the Amphibia of Oklahoma. Art III : 35–38. University of Oklahoma Press, Norman, Oklahoma.

1950b. Salientian range extensions in Oklahoma and a new state record. Researches on the Amphibia of Oklahoma. Art. IV : 39–44. University of Oklahoma Press, Norman, Oklahoma.

1950c. Observations on the ecology and natural history of Anura. XVII. Adaptations and distribution in accordance with habits in Oklahoma. Researches on the Amphibia of Oklahoma. Art. VI : 59–100. University of Oklahoma Press, Norman, Oklahoma.

* 1950d. Some adaptations of survival value in spadefoot toads. Researches on the Amphibia of Oklahoma. Art. VII :

101–116. University of Oklahoma Press, Norman, Oklahoma.

1950e Observations on Scaphiopus, 1949. The Wasmann Journal of Biology, 8 : 221–228.

1950f. A sexual difference in dermal secretions in spadefoots. Proceedings of the Oklahoma Academy of Science, 24 : 11–12.

1950g A note on the egg-mass of *Scaphiopus hurterii*. Proceedings of the Oklahoma Academy of Science, 30 : 18–19.

* 1951. Mass movement at metamorphosis in the Savannah spadefoot, *Scaphiopus hurterii* Strecker. Proceedings of the Oklahoma Academy of Science, 31 : 26–27.

*Bragg, Arthur N.

1954. Aggregational behavior and feeding reactions in tadpoles of the Savannah spadefoot. Herpetologica, 10 : 97–102.

1956. The amphibia of Greer County, Oklahoma. Great Basin Naturalist, 15 : 27–31.

1956a Notes on the behavior of toads in captivity. The Wasmann Journal of Biology, 14 : 301–310.

1956b. The spadefoot toads. The Oklahoma Quarterly, 5 : 29–32.

1956c. Further observations on spadefoot toads. Herpetologica, 12 : 201–204.

* 1956d. In quest of the spadefoots. New Mexico Quarterly, 25 : 345–357.

* 1957. Dimorphism and cannibalism in tadpoles of *Scaphiopus bombifrons*. Southwestern Naturalist, 1 : 105–108.

1957a. Amphibian eggs produced singly or in masses. Herpetologica, 13 : 212.

* 1957b. Aggregational feeding and metamorphic aggregations in tadpoles of *Scaphiopus hurterii* observed in 1954. The Wasmann Journal of Biology, 15 : 61–68.

1957c. Variations in color and color pattern in tadpoles in Oklahoma. Copeia 1957 (1) : 36–39.

1957d. Some factors in feeding of toads. Herpetologica, 13 : 189-191.

* 1958. On metamorphic and post-metamorphic aggregations in spadefoots. Herpetologica, 13 : 273.

* 1959. Behavior of tadpoles of Hurter's Spadefoot during an exceptionally rainy season. Wasmann Journal of Biology 17 : 23–42.

1959a The clasping reflex observed in juvenile spadefoots. Southwestern Naturalist, 3 : 229.

1960. Experimental observations on the feeding of spadefoot tadpoles. Southwestern Naturalist, 5 : 201–207.

* 1961. The behavior and comparative developmental rates in nature of a spadefoot, a toad and a frog. Herpetologica 17 : 73–84.

* 1961a. A theory of the origin of spadefooted toads deduced principally from a study of their habits. Animal Behaviour 9 : 178–186.

1962. Predator-prey relationship in two species of spadefoot tadpoles with notes on some other features of their behavior. The Wasmann Journal of Biology, 20 : 81–97.

1964 : Further study of predation and cannibalism in spadefoot tadpoles. Herpetologica 20 : 17–24.

Bragg, Arthur N. and William N. Bragg

1957. Parasitism of spadefoot tadpoles by Saprolegnia. Herpetologica, 13 : 191.

* 1958. Variation in the mouth parts in tadpoles of *Scaphiopus (Spea) bombifrons* Cope. (Amphibia : Salientia). The Southwestern Naturalist 3 : 55–69.

*Bragg, Arthur N. and Otis M. King

1961. Aggregational and asociated behavior in tadpoles of the Plains Spadefoot. Wasmann Journal of Biology, 18 : 273–289.

*Bragg, Arthur N. and Charles C. Smith

1942. Observations on the ecology and natural history of Anura. IX. Notes on breeding behavior in Oklahoma. The Great Basin Naturalist, 3 : 33–50.

Brandt, B. B.
  1936. The frogs and toads of eastern North Carolina. Copeia 1936 (4) : 215–223.
Brimley, C. C.
  1926. Revised key and list of the amphibians and reptiles of North Carolina. Journal of the Elisha Mitchell Zoological Society, 42 : 75–93.
Brooks, F. G.
  1930. Those Oklahoma toads. The Biologist, 1(3) : 21–22.
Brown, B. C.
  1950. An annotated check list of the reptiles and amphibians of Texas. Baylor University Press, Waco, Texas, 259 pp.
Burnett, W. N.
  1926. Notes on Colorado herpetology. Occasional Papers of the Museum of Zoology and Entomology, State Agricultural College of Colorado, 1 : 1–4.
Burt, Charles E.
  1935. Further records on the ecology and distribution of amphibians and reptiles in the Middle West. American Midland Naturalist, 16 : 311–336.
*Carr, Archie F.
  1940. A contribution to the herpetology of Florida. University of Florida Biological Science Series, 3(1) : 118 pp.
Childs, H. E., Jr.
  1953. A selection experiment in nature using albino and normal spadefoot toads. Bulliten of the Ecological Society of America, 34(2) : 48–49.
Cope, Edward D.
  1863. On Trachycephalus, Scaphiopus, and other American Batrachia. Proceedings of the Academy of Natural Science of Philadelphia, 1863 : 43–54.
Cope, Edward D.
  1879. A contribution to the biology of Montana. American Naturalist, 13 : 432–411.
  1889. Batrachia of North America. United States National Museum Bulletin, 34 : 1–525.

Decker, Charles E.
   1930. Age of the toads in the H. H. Hollman sand pit at
      Frederick, Oklahoma. Proceedings of the Oklahoma
      Academy of Science, 10 : 83–84.
Dickerson, Mary C.
   1913. The frog book. Doubleday, Page and Co., New York
      City.
Driver, E. C.
   1936. Observations on *Scaphiopus holbrooki* (Harlan). Copeia
      1936(1) : 67-69.
Duellman, William E.
   1955. Taxonomic status of the Key West spadefoot toad,
      Scaphiopus holbrooki albus. Copeia 1955(2) : 141–143.
Dunn, E. R.
   1930. Reptiles and amphibians of North Hampton and vicin-
      ity. Bulletin of the Boston Society of Natural History,
      57 : 5–8.
*Gilmore, R. J.
   1924. Notes on the life history and feeding habits of the spade-
      foot of the western plains. Colorado College Publica-
      tions, (Science Service) 13(1) : 12 pp.
Giovanolli, Leonard
   1936. *Scaphiopus holbrooki* in Kentucky. Copeia 1936(1) : 69.
*Goldsmith, G. W.
   1926. Habits and reactions of *Scaphiopus hammondi.* Carnegie
      Institute of Washington Yearbook No. 25 (1925–26) :
      369–370.
*Gosner, Kenneth and Irving H. Black
   1955. The effects of temperature and moisture on the repro-
      ductive cycle of *Scaphiopus h. holbrooki.* American
      Midland Naturalist, 54 : 192–203.
*Hansen, Keith L.
   1958. Breeding pattern of the eastern spadefoot. Herpetolo-
      gica 14 : 58–68.
* 1959. A study of *in vitro* ovulation in the eastern spadefoot,

Scaphiopus h. holbrooki. Quarterly Journal of the
Florida Academy of Science, 22 : 1–13.

Hargitt, C. W.
  1888. Recent notes on *Scaphiopus holbrookii.* American
        Naturalist, 22 : 535–537.

Halman, J. Alan
  1957. Bullfrog predation on the Eastern Spadefoot, *Scaphio-
        pus holbrooki.* Copeia 1957(3) : 229.

Kellogg, Remington
  1932. Notes on the spadefoot of the western plains *(Scaphio-
        pus hammondii).* Copeia 1932(1) : 36.

King, F. W.
  1932. Herpetological records and notes from the vicinity of
        Tucson, Arizona, July and August, 1930. Copeia
        1932(4) : 175–177.

Knepton, J. C.
  1951. The responses of male Salientia to human chorionic
        hormone. Quarterly Journal of the Florida Academy of
        Science, 14 : 255–265.

Linsdale, Jean S.
  1938. Environmental responses of vertebrates in the Great
        Basin. American Midland Naturalist, 19 : 1–206.

Little, E. L., Jr., and J. G. Keller
  1937. Amphibians and reptiles of the Granada Experimental
        Range. Copeia 1937(4) : 216–222.

*Livezey, Robert L., and A. H. Wright
  1947. A synoptic key to the Salientian eggs of the United
        States. American Midland Naturalist, 37 : 179–222.

Lowe, Charles H., Jr.
  1954. Isolating mechanisms in sympatric populations of South-
        western Anurans. Texas Journal of Science, 6 : 265–270.

*Moore, George A.
  1937. The spadefoot toad under drought conditions. Copeia
        1937(4) : 225–226.

*Neill, Wilfred T.
  1957. Notes on metamorphic and breeding aggregations of the

Eastern Spadefoot, *Scaphiopus holbrooki* (Harlan). Herpetologica, 13 : 185–187.

Nichols, A.

1852. Occurrence of *Scaphiopus solitarius* in Essex county with some notices of its history, habits, etc. Journal of the Essex County Natural History Society, 3 : 113–117.

Nichols, John

1917. Spade-foot toad at Mastic, Long Island. Copeia 45 : 59-60.

Noble, G. K.

1926. The hatching process in *Atyles, Eleutherodactylus,* and other amphibians. American Museum Novitiates, 229 : 7 pp.

*Ortenburger, A. I.

1924. Life history notes—Scaphiopus—the spadefoot toad. Proceedings of the Oklahoma Academy of Science, 4 : 19–20.

Ortenburger, A. I., and Beryl Freeman

1930. Notes on some reptiles and amphibians from western Oklahoma. Publications of the University of Oklahoma Biological Survey, 2 : 175–188.

Ortenburger, A. I., and R. D. Ortenburger

1926. Field observations on some amphibians and reptiles of Pima County, Arizona. Proceedings of the Oklahoma Academy of Science, 6(1) : 101–121.

Overton, Frank

1914. Long Island fauna and flora. 3. The frogs and toads. Museum of the Brooklyn Institute of Science, Science Bulletin, 2 : 21–40.

1915. Annual occurrence of spadefoot toads. Copeia 20 :17.

1915a. Late-breeding of spade-foot toads, etc. Copeia 24 : 52–53.

*Pearson, Paul G.

1955. Population ecology of the spadefoot, *Scaphiopus holbrooki* (Harlan). Ecological Monographs, 25 : 233–267.

Pearson, Paul G.
   1957. Further notes on the population ecology of the spade-
      foot toad. Ecology 38 : 580–586.
Pike, Nicholas
   1886. Notes on the hermit spadefoot. Bulletin of the American
      Museum of Natural History, 1(7) : 213–221.
Putnam, F. W.
   1863. Statements concerning frogs and toads about Cam-
      bridge, Massachusetts. Proceedings of the Boston Society
      of Natural History, 9 : 229–
Reed, Clyde F.
   1956. The spadefoot toad in Maryland. Herpetologica, 12(4) :
      294–295.
*Richmond, Neil D.
   1947. Life history of Scaphiopus holbrookii holbrookii (Har-
      lan). Part I : Larval development and behavior. Ecology
      28 : 53–67.
Ruthven, A. G.
   1907. A collection of reptiles and amphibians from southern
      New Mexico and Arizona. Bulletin of the American
      Museum of Natural History, 23(23) : 483–604.
Sherwood, W. L.
   1898. The frogs and toads found in the vicinity of New York
      City. Proceedings of the Linnean Society of New York,
      10 : 17–18.
Schmidt, K. P.
   1953. A check list of North American amphibians and rep-
      tiles, (Ed. 6). American Society Ichthyologists and
      Herpetologists. VIII + 280 pp.
Slevin, J. R.
   1928. The amphibians of western North America. Occasional
      Papers of the California Academy of Science 16 : 152 pp.
*Smith, F. S.
   1879. The spadefoot toad in New Haven, Connecticut. Ameri-
      can Naturalist, 13 : 651–652.

*Smith, Hobart M.
1934. The amphibians of Kansas. American Midland Naturalist, 15 : 377–525.

Smith, Hobart M. and H. K. Buechner
1947. The influence of the Balcones Escarpment on the distributions of amphibians and reptiles in Texas. Bulletin of the Chicago Academy of Science, 8(1) : 1–16.

*Smith, Hobart M. and Arthur B. Leonard
1934. Distributional records of reptiles and amphibians in Oklahoma. American Midland Naturalist, 15 : 190–196.

Smith, Hobart M. and Ottys Sanders
1952. Distributional data on Texas amphibians and reptiles. Texas Journal of Science, 1952(2) : 204–219.

Smith, Philip W., and Sherman A. Minton, Jr.
1957. A distributional summary of the herpetofauna of Indiana and Illinois. American Midland Naturalist, 58 : 341–351.

*Stebbins, R. C.
1951. Amphibians of western North America. University of California Press, Berkeley and Los Angeles, California, 539 pp.

Stine, Charles J., Robert S. Simmons, and James A. Fowler
1956. New records for the Eastern Spadefoot toad in Maryland. Herpetologica 12(4) : 295–296.

Stone, Witmer
1932. Terrestrial activity of spade-foot toads. Copeia 1932(1) : 35–36.

*Storer, Tracy I.
1925. A synopsis of the amphibia of California. University of California Publications in Zoology, 27 : 342 pp.

*Strecker, John K., Jr.
1908. The reptiles and batrachians of McLennon County, Texas. Proceedings of the Biological Society of Washington, 21 : 69–84

1908a The reptiles and batrachians of Victoria and Refugio

counties, Texas. Proceedings of the Biological Society of Washington, 21 : 47–52.

1908b A preliminary annotated list of the Batrachia of Texas. Proceedings of the Biological Society of Washington 21 : 53–61.

* 1908c. Notes on the life history of *Scaphiopus couchii* Baird. Proceedings of the Biological Society of Washington 21 : 199–206.

1910 Notes on the fauna of a portion of the Canyon regions of northwestern Texas. Baylor University Bulletin 13 : 31 pp.

* 1910a. Description of a new solitary spadefoot (*Scaphiopus hurterii*) from Texas, with other herpetological notes. Proceedings of Biological Society of Washington, 23 : 115–122.

1915. Reptiles and amphibians of Texas. Baylor Bulletin, 18 : 82 pp.

1935. A list of hitherto unpublished localities for Texas amphibians and reptiles. In Notes on the Zoology of Texas, Baylor Bulletin, 38(3) : 35–38.

*Tanner, Vasco M.

1939. A study of the genus Scaphiopus. Great Basin Naturalist, 1(1) : 3–26.

*Taylor, Edward H.

1948. Tadpoles of Mexican Anura. University of Kansas Science Bulletin, 38 : Part I (3) : 37–55.

*Trowbridge, A. H. and M. S. Trowbridge

1937. Notes on the cleavage rate of *Scaphiopus bombifrons* Cope with additional remarks on certain aspects of its life history. American Naturalist, 71 : 460–480.

*Trowbridge, Minnie S.

1941. Studies on the normal development of *Scaphiopus bombifrons* Cope, I. the cleavage period. Transactions of the American Microscopical Society, 60 : 508–526.

* 1942. Studies on the normal development of *Scaphiopus bombifrons* Cope, II. The later embryonic and larval

periods. Transactions of the American Microscopical Society, 61 : 66–83.

*Turner, Frederick B.
1952. The mouth parts of tadpoles of the spadefoot toad, *Scaphiopus hammondi*. Copeia 1952 (3) : 172–175.

*Wasserman, Aaron O.
1957. Factors affecting interbreeding in sympatric species of spadefoots (Genus Scaphiopus). Evolution, 11 (3) 320–338.

* 1957a. Hybridization in three species of spadefoot toads. Copeia 1957 (2) : 144–145.

* 1958. Relationships of allopatric populations of spadefoots (Genus Scaphiopus). Evolution 12(3) : 311–318.

Wood, W. F.
1935. Encounters with the Western Spadefoot, *Scaphiopus hammondii,* with a note on a few albino larvae. Copeia 1935 (2) : 100–102.

*Wright, A. A. and A. H. Wright
1933. Handbook on frogs and toads. Comstock Publishing Company, Ithaca, N. Y. (Ed. 2, 1942; Ed. 3, 1949)

Wright, A. H.
1929. Synopsis and description of North American tadpoles. Proceedings of the United States National Museum, 74 : 1–70.

1931. Life histories of the frogs in Okefinokee Swamp, Georgia. XV + 497 pp. The MacMillan Co., N. Y. C.

Wright, A. H. and A. A. Wright
1938. Amphibians of Texas. Transactions of the Texas Academy of Science, 21 : 35 pp.

*Zweifel, Richard G.
1956. Two pelobatid frogs from the tertiary of North America and their relationship to fossil and recent forms. American Museum Novitates 1762 : 458 pp.

Index

125

DATE DUE

OCT. 21. 1985			
GAYLORD			PRINTED IN U.S.A.